discovering
MATHEMATICS

3A

Chow Wai Keung B. Sc. (Hons), Cert. Ed., M. Soc. Sc.

General Editor: Esther Ng Yoon Cheng B. Sc. (Hons), Dip. Ed.

Consultant: Prof Ling San PhD

D1305883

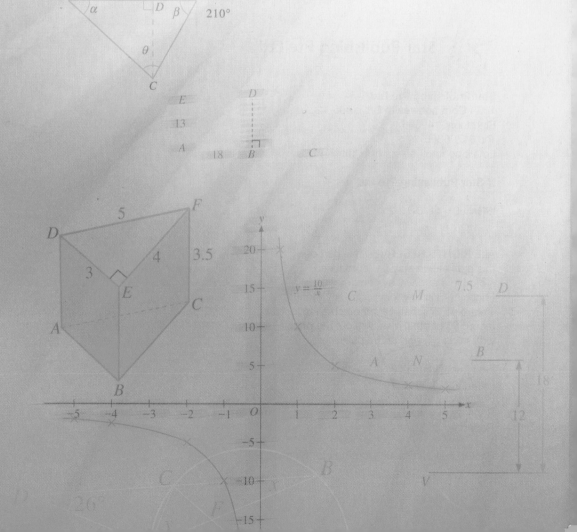

 Star Publishing Pte Ltd

Star Publishing Pte Ltd
115A Commonwealth Drive #05-12
Singapore 149596
Tel: 64796800
Email: contactus@starpub.com.sg

© **Star Publishing Pte Ltd**

ISBN 981-4176-70-2

ALL RIGHTS RESERVED. No part of
this publication may be reproduced,
stored in a retrieval system, or
transmitted in any form or by any means,
electronic, mechanical, photocopying,
recording or otherwise, without the prior
written permission of the publisher.

First published 2007
Reprinted 2008
Reprinted 2010
Reprinted 2011
Reprinted 2012

Printed by KHL Printing Co Pte Ltd, Singapore

Acknowledgements

The publisher wishes to thank the following:

The University of Cambridge Local Examinations Syndicate (UCLES) and the Singapore Examinations and Assessment Board (SEAB) for permission to reproduce selected past GCE O-level questions. The answers given in this publication are given by the publisher. UCLES and SEAB bear no responsibility for these answers. Any queries or comments on the answers should be forwarded to the publisher directly.

The Geometer's Sketchpad, Key Curriculum Press, 1150 65th Street, Emeryville, CA 94608, www.keypress.com for permission to use the screenshots of activities created using The Geometer's Sketchpad.

Photo Credits

Chapter 1   Pg 1   Saturn and the Solar System orbits, Photolibrary
               Pg 18   Formica fusca ants communicating,
                           Dust mite,
                           Red and white blood cells and platelets,
                           Computer model of part of DNA molecule,
                           Bacteria on the point of a pin,
                           Micromechanical chain, Photolibrary;
               Pg 18   Model of nanotube, Corbis;

Chapter 2   Pg 29   Sports car, Photolibrary
               Pg 36   Dolphin leaping from surface of the sea, Photolibrary

Chapter 4   Pg 74   Sail boats on the beach, Photolibrary

Chapter 5   Pg 134   An assortment of pharmaceutical tablets and capsules, Photolibrary
               Pg 136   Antibiotics tested in a bacterial culture, Photolibrary

Chapter 6   Pg 157   A display of alloy wheels, Stamford Tyres International Pte Ltd

PREFACE

Discovering Mathematics is a series of textbooks designed for the students in secondary schools. It follows the secondary Mathematics syllabus issued by the Ministry of Education, Singapore, which will be implemented from 2007 onwards. This series of Mathematics books covers the entire syllabus for the Singapore-Cambridge GCE O-Level Mathematics.

The emphasis of this series is on empowering students to learn mathematics effectively and independently. Depending on the topics covered, different approaches are adopted for the presentation of concepts to facilitate easy understanding by students. In some topics, an intuitive or an experimental approach is adopted to enable students to internalise concepts and instil in them an interest to explore the topics further.

Each book includes appropriate examples, class activities and diagrams to enable students to understand the concepts and apply them. IT skills and NE values are incorporated as appropriate.

Key Features:

- **Chapter Opener**

  A chapter opener starts the chapter by featuring some history about the topic or drawing a connection between mathematics and real life situations. The opener also lists the learning objectives for the chapter.

- **Class Activities**

  Class activities allow students to learn mathematics through discovery. Some of these activities make use of computer software to make the learning of mathematics dynamic and interactive.

- **Examples and Try It!**

  Worked examples are included to facilitate students' understanding of concepts and to show how ideas can be expressed clearly in writing in the presentation of solutions. After each worked example, a similar question (Try It!) is provided so that students can try it out and check if they have understood the concept(s) presented earlier.

- **Exercises**

  Every section of a chapter presents an exercise for the students. The questions in the exercises are sequenced as *Basic Practice*, *Further Practice*, *Maths@Work* and *Brainworks*. Simple questions involving a direct application of the concepts are given in *Basic Practice*. More challenging questions on direct application are given in *Further Practice*. *Maths@Work* presents some questions that apply mathematical concepts to real-life situations. Questions involving higher order thinking or an open-ended approach to problems are given in *Brainworks*. These questions encourage students to think analytically, to be creative and to come up with solutions of their own.

  A Revision Exercise at the end of each chapter enables students to revise the concepts taught and to help consolidate their learning.

- **Problem-solving Processes And Heuristics**
  A list of the general processes and the heuristics for problem-solving is provided after the last chapter in each book. Some worked examples illustrating the use of some of the heuristics are included as well.

- **In A Nutshell**
  A summary of the important concepts in each chapter is provided for recap and revision by the students.

- **Extend Your Learning Curve**
  This includes questions or investigative activities designed to encourage students to explore mathematical concepts further or apply mathematics in real-life situations.

- **Write In Your Journal**
  Questions are posed to encourage students to reflect on their learning experience in each chapter.

In addition, the series has the following features, indicated in the right margin.

- **Remark**
  Important information that is of interest to students is included as appropriate.

- **Recall**
  Concepts or definitions covered earlier and related to the material just discussed are included to help students recall them.

- **Discuss**
  Questions concerning the concepts being taught are included in appropriate sections to encourage discussion between the teacher and the students.

- **MathsBits**
  Interesting questions, puzzles or facts that are related to mathematics, mathematicians or the history of mathematics are also featured as appropriate.

- **Go Online**
  Some website references are provided for students to access and gather more information on their own. For an update of the website references, students may visit the company's web page http://www.starpub.com.sg/Secondary/Maths.

I hope that with this comprehensive series, students will find learning mathematics an easy and fun experience so that they will be motivated to study the subject, discover mathematical features and apply them in real-life situations.

My sincere thanks go to all those who have provided valuable feedback and great assistance in the production of this series.

Chow Wai Keung

CONTENTS

1 Indices

The Earth is one of the planets of our Solar System. Do you know the distance between the Earth and the Sun? How can we express this distance using as few digits as possible?

Let's learn to...

- state and apply the laws of indices
- state the definitions of zero and negative and fractional indices
- simplify an expression involving indices
- express numbers in standard form
- be aware of rounding and truncation errors in a calculator for very small and very large numbers
- solve equations involving indices

1.1 Positive Indices And Laws Of Indices

We learnt that a number a when multiplied by itself n times can be represented in the index notation a^n.

$$a^n = \underbrace{a \times a \times \ldots \times a}_{n \text{ factors}}, \text{ where } n \text{ is a positive integer.}$$

In the notation a^n, a is called the **base**, n is called the **index** or **exponent**, and a^n is read as "the nth **power** of a" or "a to the **power** of n".

For example,

$$8^3 = 8 \times 8 \times 8 = 512,$$

$$\left(\frac{3}{5}\right)^4 = \frac{3}{5} \times \frac{3}{5} \times \frac{3}{5} \times \frac{3}{5} = \frac{81}{625}.$$

There are some laws that enable us to manipulate numbers in index notation. Let us investigate to find out what these laws are.

Class Activity 1

Express the following manipulations in index notation. The first one in each set has been done for you. Assume that m and n are positive integers, $m > n$, and $a \neq 0$.

1. **(a)** $7^2 \times 7^3 = (7 \times 7) \times (7 \times 7 \times 7) \qquad = 7^5$

   (b) $2^3 \times 2^5 = (2 \times 2 \times 2) \times (2 \times 2 \times 2 \times 2 \times 2) = 2^{\boxed{}}$

   (c) $a^4 \times a^3 = (a \times a \times a \times a) \times (a \times a \times a) \qquad = a^{\boxed{}}$

   (d) $a^m \times a^2$

   (e) $a^m \times a^n$

2. **(a)** $5^6 \div 5^2 = \dfrac{\cancel{5} \times \cancel{5} \times 5 \times 5 \times 5 \times 5}{\cancel{5} \times \cancel{5}} \qquad = 5^4$

   (b) $8^7 \div 8^4 = \dfrac{8 \times 8 \times 8 \times 8 \times 8 \times 8 \times 8}{8 \times 8 \times 8 \times 8} \qquad = 8^{\boxed{}}$

   In **2(a)**, 5×5 are cancelled in the numerator and in the denominator.

   (c) $c^5 \div c^3$

   (d) $b^m \div b^2$

   (e) $a^m \div a^n$

3. **(a)** $(9^2)^3 = 9^2 \times 9^2 \times 9^2$ $\qquad\qquad = 9^6$

   (b) $(3^5)^4 = 3^5 \times 3^5 \times 3^5 \times 3^5$ $\qquad = 3^{\boxed{}}$

   (c) $(x^2)^5$

   (d) $(y^m)^3$

   (e) $(a^m)^n$

The results of Class Activity 1 reveal the following **laws of indices**.

If m and n are positive integers where $m > n$ and $a \neq 0$, then

1. $a^m \times a^n = a^{m+n}$;
2. $a^m \div a^n = a^{m-n}$;
3. $(a^m)^n = a^{mn}$.

Example 1   Simplify the following.
           (a) $a^5 \times a^7$ **(b)** $(3p^2q) \times (4p^6q^8)$

Solution   **(a)** $a^5 \times a^7 = a^{5+7}$ $a^m \times a^n = a^{m+n}$
                      $= a^{12}$

          (b) $(3p^2q) \times (4p^6q^8) = (3 \times 4)(p^2 \times p^6)(q \times q^8)$ rearrange like factors
                                  $= 12p^{2+6}q^{1+8}$ $q = q^1$
                                    $= 12p^8q^9$

▶ *Try It 1!*   Simplify the following.
           (a) $a^{10} \times a^8$ **(b)** $(5x^3y^4) \times (6xy^7)$

Example 2   Simplify the following.
           (a) $p^{13} \div p^6$ **(b)** $(-24a^5b^4) \div (3a^2b^3)$

Solution   **(a)** $p^{13} \div p^6 = p^{13-6}$ $a^m \div a^n = a^{m-n}$
                      $= p^7$

          (b) $(-24a^5b^4) \div (3a^2b^3) = \left(\dfrac{-24}{3}\right)\left(\dfrac{a^5}{a^2}\right)\left(\dfrac{b^4}{b^3}\right)$ rearrange like factors
                                      $= -8a^{5-2}b^{4-3}$
                                      $= -8a^3b$

▶ *Try It 2!*   Simplify the following.
           (a) $q^{17} \div q^{11}$ **(b)** $(30r^9s^{10}) \div (6r^8s^3)$

Example 3   Simplify the following.
(a) $(x^7)^6$
(b) $(y^5)^3 \div (y^2)^4$

Solution   (a) $(x^7)^6 = x^{7 \times 6}$ $(a^m)^n = a^{mn}$
$= x^{42}$

(b) $(y^5)^3 \div (y^2)^4 = y^{5 \times 3} \div y^{2 \times 4}$
$= y^{15} \div y^8$
$= y^{15-8}$
$= y^7$

▶ *Try It 3!*   Simplify the following.
(a) $(b^9)^5$
(b) $(c^6)^8 \div (c^3)^{10}$

Class Activity 2

Rewrite each of the following as a product or a quotient in index notation. The first one in each set has been done for you. Assume that n is a positive integer, $k \neq 0$, $y \neq 0$ and $b \neq 0$.

1. (a) $(4 \times 5)^2 = (4 \times 5) \times (4 \times 5)$ $= 4^2 \times 5^2$

(b) $(2 \times c)^3 = (2 \times c) \times (2 \times c) \times (2 \times c) = 2^{\boxed{}} \times c^{\boxed{}}$

(c) $(pq)^4$

(d) $(ab)^n$

2. (a) $\left(\dfrac{2}{3}\right)^2 = \dfrac{2}{3} \times \dfrac{2}{3} = \dfrac{2^2}{3^2}$ (b) $\left(\dfrac{7}{k}\right)^3$

(c) $\left(\dfrac{x}{y}\right)^5$ (d) $\left(\dfrac{a}{b}\right)^n$

The results of Class Activity 2 yield another two **laws of indices**.

> If n is a positive integer, then
>
> 4. $(ab)^n = a^n b^n$;
>
> 5. $\left(\dfrac{a}{b}\right)^n = \dfrac{a^n}{b^n}$,   where $b \neq 0$.

Example 4   Simplify the following.

(a) $(c^4d^5)^3 \times (c^2d^7)^6$

(b) $\left(\dfrac{2x^4}{y}\right)^5 \div \left(\dfrac{-4x}{y^2}\right)^3$

Find 2 integers, m and n, such that $m^n = n^m$, where $m > 0$ and $n > 0$.

Solution   (a) $(c^4d^5)^3 \times (c^2d^7)^6 = c^{4 \times 3}d^{5 \times 3} \times c^{2 \times 6}d^{7 \times 6}$ $(ab)^n = a^n b^n$

$\qquad\qquad\qquad\qquad\qquad = c^{12}d^{15} \times c^{12}d^{42}$

$\qquad\qquad\qquad\qquad\qquad = c^{12+12}d^{15+42}$ $a^m \times a^n = a^{m+n}$

$\qquad\qquad\qquad\qquad\qquad = c^{24}d^{57}$

(b) $\left(\dfrac{2x^4}{y}\right)^5 \div \left(\dfrac{-4x}{y^2}\right)^3 = \dfrac{2^5 x^{4 \times 5}}{y^5} \div \dfrac{(-4)^3 x^3}{y^{2 \times 3}}$ $\left(\dfrac{a}{b}\right)^n = \dfrac{a^n}{b^n}$

$\qquad\qquad\qquad\qquad\qquad = \dfrac{32x^{20}}{y^5} \div \dfrac{-64x^3}{y^6}$

$\qquad\qquad\qquad\qquad\qquad = \dfrac{32x^{20}}{y^5} \times \dfrac{y^6}{-64x^3}$ $\dfrac{A}{B} \div \dfrac{C}{D} = \dfrac{A}{B} \times \dfrac{D}{C}$

$\qquad\qquad\qquad\qquad\qquad = \dfrac{32}{-64}(x^{20-3})(y^{6-5})$ $a^m \div a^n = a^{m-n}$

$\qquad\qquad\qquad\qquad\qquad = -\dfrac{x^{17}y}{2}$

▶ *Try It 4!*   Simplify the following.

(a) $(p^2q^5)^4 \times (p^3q)^6$

(b) $\left(\dfrac{3a^5}{b^3}\right)^4 \div \left(\dfrac{-9a^3}{b^6}\right)^2$

Exercise 1.1

(**Basic Practice**)

1. Simplify the following and express your answers in index notation.
   (a) $3^5 \times 3^7$
   (b) $2^{10} \div 2^6$
   (c) $(5^2)^4$
   (d) $(6^3)^7$
   (e) $(4 \times 7)^8$
   (f) $(3^2 \times 11)^4$
   (g) $\left(\dfrac{8}{13}\right)^5$
   (h) $\left(\dfrac{7}{2^3}\right)^6$

2. Simplify the following.
   (a) $a^4 \times a^7$
   (b) $c^8 \div c^5$
   (c) $(e^4)^5$
   (d) $(f^7)^3$
   (e) $(pq)^9$
   (f) $(r^2s^3)^4$
   (g) $\left(\dfrac{t}{u}\right)^6$
   (h) $\left(\dfrac{v^5}{w^4}\right)^{11}$

3. Simplify the following.

    (a) $5a^6 \times 3a^2$

    (b) $(-8b^3) \times (4b^9)$

    (c) $24c^8 \div (-6c^5)$

    (d) $(-72d^{17}) \div (-4d^{13})$

    (e) $(-2e^3)^4$

    (f) $(-2r^6 s^4)^4$

    (g) $\left(\dfrac{-3u^2}{v} \right)^6$

    (h) $\left(\dfrac{4x^7}{y^8} \right)^3$

Further Practice

4. Simplify the following.

    (a) $a^7 b^4 \times a^5 b^6$

    (b) $c^{12} d^9 \div c^{10} d^8$

    (c) $(3e^2 f) \times (4e^9 f^7)$

    (d) $(15g^8 h^7) \div (5g^2 h^4)$

    (e) $(-18m^3 n^5) \div (24m^2 n)$

    (f) $\left(-\dfrac{8p^7}{q^2} \right) \times \left(-\dfrac{q^9}{p^4} \right)$

    (g) $\left(\dfrac{3s^9}{t^3} \right) \div \left(-\dfrac{6s^5}{t^8} \right)$

    (h) $(u^3 v^4)^5 \times (u^2 v^7)^3$

    (i) $(w^3 x^4)^6 \div (-w^2 x^3)^5$

    (j) $\left(\dfrac{2y^3}{z} \right)^7 \times \left(\dfrac{z^6}{4y^{10}} \right)^2$

5. Simplify the following.

    (a) $5a^4 \times 3a^2 \div a^3$

    (b) $(b^3 c^8) \div (b^2 c^5) \times (b^7 c^{11})$

    (c) $(5mn^3)^3 (6m^2 n^9) \div (3m^2 n^4)^2$

    (d) $\left(\dfrac{2x^4}{y} \right)^4 \div \left(\dfrac{3x^2}{y^3} \right)^5 \times \left(\dfrac{6y^5}{x} \right)^2$

Maths@Work

6. A person sent 2^{13} copies of a junk mail via email. Each email consisted of 2^{11} bytes of data. How many bytes of data were sent altogether? Express your answer in index notation.

Brainworks

7. If $(a^m)^n = a^{231}$, where m and n are positive integers greater than 1, and $m < n$, find two possible sets of values of m and n.

1.2 Zero And Negative Integral Indices

When n is a positive integer, a^n means 'a is multiplied by itself n times'. However, when n is zero or a negative integer, a^n is not defined in the same way. Let us investigate its meaning and discover the rules that apply to zero and negative integral indices in the following class activity.

Class Activity 3

Suppose $a \neq 0$ and we assume the following:
- a^0, a^{-1}, a^{-2}, a^{-3}, ... exist
- the laws of indices are valid for these powers of a
- n is a positive integer

Let us perform the following calculations.

1. **(a)** By the laws of indices,
$$2^5 \div 2^5 = 2^{\boxed{} - \boxed{}} = 2^{\boxed{}}$$

   By direct calculation,
   $$2^5 \div 2^5 = \frac{2 \times 2 \times 2 \times 2 \times 2}{2 \times 2 \times 2 \times 2 \times 2} = \boxed{}$$
   $$\therefore \quad 2^0 = \boxed{}$$

   (b) By the laws of indices,
   $$a^3 \div a^3 = a^{\boxed{} - \boxed{}} = a^{\boxed{}}$$

   By direct calculation,
   $$a^3 \div a^3 = \frac{a \times a \times a}{a \times a \times a} = \boxed{}$$
   $$\therefore \quad a^0 = \boxed{}$$

2. **(a)** $7^3 \div 7^5 = 7^{\boxed{} - \boxed{}} = 7^{\boxed{}}$

   But $\dfrac{7^3}{7^5} = \dfrac{7 \times 7 \times 7}{7 \times 7 \times 7 \times 7 \times 7} = \boxed{}$

   $\therefore \ 7^{-2} = \dfrac{1}{7^{\boxed{}}}$

   (b) $a^4 \div a^7 = a^{\boxed{} - \boxed{}} = a^{\boxed{}}$

   $\dfrac{a^4}{a^7} = \dfrac{a \times a \times a \times a}{a \times a \times a \times a \times a \times a \times a} = \dfrac{1}{a^{\boxed{}}}$

   $\therefore \ a^{-3} = \dfrac{1}{a^{\boxed{}}}$

From Class Activity 3, we observe that for the laws of indices to apply to zero and negative integral indices, we have to define the following rules.

When $a \neq 0$ and n is a positive integer,

$$a^0 = 1$$

and $$a^{-n} = \frac{1}{a^n}.$$

Note: $0^0, 0^{-1}, 0^{-2}, \ldots$ are undefined.

Example 5 Evaluate the following.

(a) $2^{-3} + 5^0$

(b) $7^{-5} \times 7^4$

(c) $(3^4)^{-3} \div (3^{-2})^5$

(d) $\left(\dfrac{5}{4}\right)^{-2}$

Solution

(a) $2^{-3} + 5^0 = \dfrac{1}{2^3} + 1$ $a^{-n} = \dfrac{1}{a^n}$ and $a^0 = 1$

$\phantom{2^{-3} + 5^0} = \dfrac{1}{8} + 1$

$\phantom{2^{-3} + 5^0} = 1\dfrac{1}{8}$

(b) $7^{-5} \times 7^4 = 7^{-5+4}$

$\phantom{7^{-5} \times 7^4} = 7^{-1}$

$\phantom{7^{-5} \times 7^4} = \dfrac{1}{7}$

(c) $(3^4)^{-3} \div (3^{-2})^5 = 3^{4 \times (-3)} \div 3^{(-2) \times 5}$

$\phantom{(3^4)^{-3} \div (3^{-2})^5} = 3^{-12} \div 3^{-10}$

$\phantom{(3^4)^{-3} \div (3^{-2})^5} = 3^{-12-(-10)}$

$\phantom{(3^4)^{-3} \div (3^{-2})^5} = 3^{-2}$

$\phantom{(3^4)^{-3} \div (3^{-2})^5} = \dfrac{1}{3^2}$

$\phantom{(3^4)^{-3} \div (3^{-2})^5} = \dfrac{1}{9}$

(d) $\left(\dfrac{5}{4}\right)^{-2} = \dfrac{1}{\left(\dfrac{5}{4}\right)^2}$

$\phantom{\left(\dfrac{5}{4}\right)^{-2}} = \dfrac{1}{\dfrac{25}{16}}$

$\phantom{\left(\dfrac{5}{4}\right)^{-2}} = \dfrac{16}{25}$

Note: $\left(\dfrac{5}{4}\right)^{-2} = \left(\dfrac{4}{5}\right)^{2}$. In general, $\left(\dfrac{a}{b}\right)^{-n} = \left(\dfrac{b}{a}\right)^{n}$.

$a^{-1} = \dfrac{1}{a^1}$.

$\dfrac{1}{a^1}$ *is usually written*

as $\dfrac{1}{a}$.

Remark

Try It 5! Evaluate the following.

(a) $11^0 - 3^{-2}$ (b) $5^{-9} \times 5^6$

(c) $(2^{-9})^5 \div (2^6)^{-7}$ (d) $\left(\dfrac{7}{6}\right)^{-1}$

Example 6   Simplify the following and express your answers in positive index notation.

(a) $(a^{-3}b^4)^{-2}$ (b) $(x^4y^{-3})(x^{-6}y^3)$

(c) $(18p^9q^{-7}) \div (6p^{-2}q^{-4})$

Solution   (a) $\begin{aligned}(a^{-3}b^4)^{-2} &= (a^{-3})^{-2}(b^4)^{-2} \\ &= a^6b^{-8} \\ &= \dfrac{a^6}{b^8}\end{aligned}$ $\begin{aligned} (ab)^n &= a^n b^n \\ (a^m)^n &= a^{mn} \\ b^{-n} &= \dfrac{1}{b^n}\end{aligned}$

(b) $\begin{aligned}(x^4y^{-3})(x^{-6}y^3) &= x^{4+(-6)}y^{-3+3} \\ &= x^{-2}y^0 \\ &= \dfrac{1}{x^2}\end{aligned}$ $y^0 = 1$

(c) $\begin{aligned}(18p^9q^{-7}) \div (6p^{-2}q^{-4}) &= \dfrac{18p^9q^{-7}}{6p^{-2}q^{-4}} \\ &= 3p^{9-(-2)}q^{-7-(-4)} \\ &= 3p^{11}q^{-3} \\ &= \dfrac{3p^{11}}{q^3}\end{aligned}$

 Try It 6! Simplify the following and express your answers in positive index notation.

(a) $(m^{-4}n^3)^{-5}$ (b) $(p^6q^{-2})(p^{-6}q^{-3})$

(c) $(5x^{-4}y^8) \div (15x^{-3}y^6)$

Exercise 1.2

(Basic Practice)

1. Evaluate the following.

(a) $13^0 - 2^{-3}$ (b) $\left(\dfrac{1}{4}\right)^{-3}$

(c) $\left(\dfrac{2}{7}\right)^{-1} + 9^0$ (d) $8^{-6} \times 8^4$

(e) $7^{-10} \div 7^{-10}$ (f) $(4^{11})^0$

(g) $(3^{-9})^4 \times (3^{-5})^{-7}$ (h) $(2^5)^{-6} \div (2^{-9})^3$

2. Simplify the following and express your answers in positive index notation.

   (a) $a^2 \div a^5$

   (b) $b^3 \times b^{-4}$

   (c) $(3^{-2}e^4)^{-1}$

   (d) $(f^{-5}g^3)^2$

   (e) $\left(\dfrac{5^{-3}}{h^2}\right)^{-2}$

   (f) $(p^{-2}q^3)(p^{-4}q^{-3})$

   (g) $(r^3 s^{-1})(r^{-9} s^6)$

   (h) $(x^4 y^3) \div (x^{-5} y^8)$

Further Practice

3. Simplify the following and express your answers in positive index notation.

   (a) $1 \div (5^2 a^{-6})^{-2}$

   (b) $(3^{-4}b^5)^{-1}(3^{-1}b^2)^2$

   (c) $\dfrac{(4c^3 d^{-1})^4}{2^{-1}c^{-2}d^5}$

   (d) $\left(\dfrac{e^3}{f^2}\right)^{-3} \times \left(\dfrac{e^{-4}}{f}\right)^{-1}$

   (e) $(m^3 n^{-4})^3 \div (m^{-5} n^{-6})$

   (f) $(3p^{-3}q^{-1})^2 \times (-4p^3 q^{-2})^2$

   (g) $\dfrac{(r^{-3} s^{-4})^{-3}}{(r^{-2} s^{-5})^{-6}}$

   (h) $(x^{-2}y)^{-5} \times \left(\dfrac{x^3}{y^2}\right)^{-4}$

Maths@Work

4. At time t hours after an injection, the amount of a drug remaining in a cell is $a^4 t^{-2}$ units, while the number of such cells in the body is $a^5 t^{-1}$, where a is a positive constant. Find the total amount of the drug remaining in the body, expressing your answer in positive index notation.

Brainworks

5. Is $(-9)^0 = -9^0$? Explain your answer.

6. Suppose $a > 0$ and n is a positive integer. Is $\left(\dfrac{1}{a}\right)^{-n} = \dfrac{1}{a^{-n}}$? Explain your answer.

1.3 Fractional Indices

A. *n*th Root of a Positive Number

We have learnt the definitions of the square root and the cube root of a positive number. For example,

$$\sqrt{25} = 5 \qquad \text{since} \quad 5^2 = 25,$$

and $\qquad \sqrt[3]{64} = 4 \qquad \text{since} \quad 4^3 = 64.$

We can extend these definitions to define the *n*th root of a positive number.

Let *a* be a positive number and *n* be a positive integer. If there exists a positive number *r* such that $r^n = a$, then *r* is called the **positive *n*th root** of *a*, and we write $r = \sqrt[n]{a}$.

When we talk about the square root of a number, we usually refer to the positive root.

Recall

Example 7 Evaluate the following.

(a) $\sqrt[4]{2401}$

(b) $\sqrt[5]{\dfrac{32}{243}}$

Solution (a) Let $\qquad r = \sqrt[4]{2401}$.

Then $\qquad r^4 = 2401$ $\qquad$ By prime factorisation,
$\qquad\qquad r^4 = 7^4$ $\qquad\qquad 2401 = 7 \times 7 \times 7 \times 7.$

$\therefore \qquad\qquad r = 7$

i.e. $\sqrt[4]{2401} = 7.$

(b) Let $\qquad x = \sqrt[5]{\dfrac{32}{243}}$.

Then $\qquad x^5 = \dfrac{32}{243}$ $\qquad$ By prime factorisation,

$\qquad\qquad x^5 = \dfrac{2^5}{3^5}$ $\qquad\qquad \dfrac{32}{243} = \dfrac{2 \times 2 \times 2 \times 2 \times 2}{3 \times 3 \times 3 \times 3 \times 3}.$

$\qquad\qquad x^5 = \left(\dfrac{2}{3}\right)^5$

$\therefore \qquad\qquad x = \dfrac{2}{3}$

i.e. $\sqrt[5]{\dfrac{32}{243}} = \dfrac{2}{3}.$

Note: We may use the function key $\boxed{\sqrt[x]{}}$ in a calculator to find the *x*th root of a number. The key sequence to evaluate $\sqrt[4]{2401}$ is:

$$4 \quad \boxed{\sqrt[x]{}} \quad 2401 \quad \boxed{=} \quad .$$

The key sequence may vary depending on the model of the calculator.

▶ _Try It **7**!_ Evaluate the value of each of the following.

(a) $\sqrt[4]{16}$

(b) $\sqrt[5]{\dfrac{1024}{3125}}$

B. Fractional Indices

Suppose a is a positive number and the laws of indices are also valid for fractional indices.

Then

$$a^{\frac{1}{2}} \times a^{\frac{1}{2}} = a^{\frac{1}{2}+\frac{1}{2}}$$

$$= a$$

$$(a^{\frac{1}{2}})^2 = a$$

∴

$$a^{\frac{1}{2}} = \sqrt{a}.$$

Similarly, $a^{\frac{1}{3}} \times a^{\frac{1}{3}} \times a^{\frac{1}{3}} = a$

$$(a^{\frac{1}{3}})^3 = a$$

Hence

$$a^{\frac{1}{3}} = \sqrt[3]{a}.$$

We can generalise this as the following definition for cases involving fractional indices.

> If a is a positive number and n is a positive integer,
>
> then $a^{\frac{1}{n}} = \sqrt[n]{a}$.

When m and n are integers, and $n > 0$, $a^{\frac{m}{n}}$ can be expressed as follows:

$$a^{\frac{m}{n}} = (a^m)^{\frac{1}{n}} \quad \text{or} \quad a^{\frac{m}{n}} = (a^{\frac{1}{n}})^m.$$

From the above definition, we have

$$a^{\frac{m}{n}} = \sqrt[n]{a^m} \quad \text{or} \quad a^{\frac{m}{n}} = (\sqrt[n]{a})^m.$$

Therefore, we arrive at another definition involving fractional indices.

> When m and n are integers, $n > 0$, and a is a positive number,
>
> $$a^{\frac{m}{n}} = \sqrt[n]{a^m} = (\sqrt[n]{a})^m.$$

Since this definition is only defined for $a > 0$, we shall assume that all the bases in index notation are positive in this chapter.

Example 8   Evaluate the following.

(a) $81^{\frac{3}{4}}$

(b) $32^{-\frac{4}{5}}$

Solution   (a) $81^{\frac{3}{4}} = (\sqrt[4]{81})^3$

$= 3^3$

$= 27$

(b) $32^{-\frac{4}{5}} = (\sqrt[5]{32})^{-4}$

$= 2^{-4}$

$= \dfrac{1}{2^4}$

$= \dfrac{1}{16}$

Note: The key sequence to calculate $32^{-\frac{4}{5}}$ is 5 $\sqrt[x]{}$ 32 x^y $+/-$ 4 .

The key sequence may vary depending on the model of the calculator.

▶ *Try It 8!*   Evaluate the following.

(a) $16^{\frac{5}{4}}$

(b) $125^{-\frac{4}{3}}$

Example 9   Simplify the following and express your answers in positive index notation.

(a) $(a^{\frac{2}{3}})^4 \times a^{\frac{1}{3}}$

(b) $(x^{\frac{3}{4}} y^{\frac{5}{2}}) \div (x^{-2} y^3)$

Solution   (a) $(a^{\frac{2}{3}})^4 \times a^{\frac{1}{3}} = a^{\frac{8}{3}} \times a^{\frac{1}{3}}$

$= a^{\frac{8}{3} + \frac{1}{3}}$

$= a^3$

(b) $(x^{\frac{3}{4}} y^{\frac{5}{2}}) \div (x^{-2} y^3) = \dfrac{x^{\frac{3}{4}} y^{\frac{5}{2}}}{x^{-2} y^3}$

$$= x^{\frac{3}{4} - (-2)} \, y^{\frac{5}{2} - 3}$$

$$= x^{\frac{11}{4}} \, y^{-\frac{1}{2}}$$

$$= \dfrac{x^{\frac{11}{4}}}{y^{\frac{1}{2}}}$$

▶ *Try It 9!* Simplify the following and express your answers in positive index notation.

(a) $(p^{\frac{5}{6}})^2 \times p^{\frac{1}{3}}$

(b) $(x^{\frac{3}{2}} y^{-4}) \div (x^{\frac{5}{3}} y^{-\frac{9}{2}})$

Exercise 1.3

(**Basic Practice**)

1. Evaluate the following.

   (a) $\sqrt{289}$

   (b) $\sqrt[3]{125}$

   (c) $\sqrt[4]{81}$

   (d) $\sqrt[5]{243}$

   (e) $(\sqrt{121})^3$

   (f) $(\sqrt[3]{216})^2$

   (g) $\sqrt[5]{\dfrac{1}{32}}$

   (h) $\sqrt[4]{\dfrac{16}{625}}$

2. Evaluate the following.

   (a) $144^{\frac{1}{2}}$

   (b) $27^{\frac{1}{3}}$

   (c) $625^{\frac{1}{4}}$

   (d) $32^{\frac{1}{5}}$

   (e) $49^{\frac{3}{2}}$

   (f) $125^{\frac{4}{3}}$

   (g) $16^{-\frac{3}{4}}$

   (h) $1331^{-\frac{2}{3}}$

   (i) $512^{-\frac{4}{9}}$

   (j) $\left(\dfrac{100}{169}\right)^{-\frac{1}{2}}$

3. Express the following in index notation.

   (a) $\sqrt{a}$ (b) $\sqrt[3]{a^2}$ (c) $\sqrt[4]{a^8}$ (d) $\sqrt[6]{a^9}$

   (e) $\dfrac{1}{\sqrt[5]{a}}$ (f) $\dfrac{1}{\sqrt[4]{a^3}}$ (g) $\dfrac{1}{(\sqrt{a})^5}$ (h) $\dfrac{1}{(\sqrt[3]{a^2})^6}$

4. Simplify the following and express your answers with positive indices.

   (a) $a^{\frac{1}{2}} \times a^{\frac{1}{3}}$ (b) $b^{\frac{3}{10}} \times b^{\frac{2}{5}}$

   (c) $c^{-\frac{1}{4}} \div c^{\frac{1}{8}}$ (d) $d^{\frac{3}{2}} \div d^{-\frac{7}{6}}$

   (e) $(e^{-3}f^4)^{-\frac{1}{2}}$ (f) $(g^{\frac{2}{3}}h^{-\frac{4}{5}})^{\frac{3}{2}}$

Further Practice

5. Simplify the following and express your answers with positive indices.

   (a) $(a^4b^3)^{\frac{1}{2}} \times (a^2b^{-5})^{\frac{1}{3}}$ (b) $(m^{-7}n^{-\frac{1}{2}})^2 \times (m^3n^{-3})^{-\frac{1}{3}}$

   (c) $\dfrac{(p^{-\frac{1}{2}}q^3)^{\frac{1}{2}}}{p^{\frac{1}{4}}q^{-5}}$ (d) $\dfrac{r^{-\frac{1}{3}}s^{-\frac{1}{4}}}{(r^2s^{-\frac{1}{2}})^{-3}}$

   (e) $\sqrt[3]{u^3v} \times (u^{-\frac{1}{2}}v^{\frac{1}{3}})^2$ (f) $(36p^2q^4)^{\frac{1}{2}}(49p^{-\frac{1}{3}}q^4)^{-\frac{1}{2}}$

   (g) $\sqrt[4]{\sqrt[3]{u^2}}$ (h) $(4x^{-\frac{1}{3}}y^{\frac{1}{2}})^{\frac{1}{3}} \div (32^{-1}x^2y^{\frac{1}{2}})^{-\frac{1}{3}}$

Maths@Work

6. A closed cuboid is $x^{\frac{1}{2}}$ cm long, $x^{\frac{1}{3}}$ cm wide and $x^{\frac{1}{4}}$ cm high.
   (a) Express the volume of the cuboid in terms of x.
   (b) Express the total surface area of the cuboid in terms of x.
   (c) Given $x = 4096$, find
      (i) the volume of the cuboid,
      (ii) the total surface area of the cuboid.

Brainworks

7. Find two possible pairs of values of p and q such that $a^p \times a^q = a^{\frac{2}{3}}$ and $(a^p)^q = -a^{-\frac{5}{3}}$.

1.4 Standard Form

A. Representation of Very Small or Very Large Numbers

Measurements in science may be very small or very large. For example, the distance between the Earth and the Sun is about 150 000 000 km, and the mass of a dust particle is about 0.000 000 000 763 kg.

Scientists have developed a concise method to express these very large and very small numbers so that we can easily manipulate and remember them. Instead of writing many trailing or leading zeros, we can write:

- 150 000 000 km as 1.5×10^8 km;
- 0.000 000 000 763 kg as 7.63×10^{-10} kg.

> A number expressed in the form
>
> $$A \times 10^n,$$
>
> where $1 \leqslant A < 10$ and n is an integer, is called the **standard form** of the number.

Standard form of a number is also called scientific notation of a number.

Remark

The standard form of a number has an advantage over the ordinary notation of that number in that it indicates the number of significant figures of that number. For example, 1.5×10^8 has 2 significant figures. However, we may not be sure of the number of significant figures of 150 000 000. The zeros after the digit 5 may or may not be significant.

Tourism statistics are often expressed in standard form. For example, in 2004, the total passenger traffic at Changi Airport was 3×10^7. With the upcoming terminal, T3, the increasing volume of passenger traffic expected at Changi Airport each year will be better managed.

MathsBits

Example 10   Express the following numbers in standard form.
(a) 6 120 000   (b) 0.000 840

Solution   (a) **STEP 1** Put the decimal point after the first digit and drop the four non-significant zeros to get the number A.

$$6.12\,0\,000$$
$$\underbrace{\qquad}_{6 \text{ places}}$$

STEP 2 Count the number of places from the decimal point to the end of the original number to get the index of the base 10.

Hence $6\,120\,000 = 6.12 \times 10^6$.

(b) STEP **1** Put the decimal point after the first non-zero digit to get the number A.

$$0.000\ 8.40$$

$$\underbrace{\qquad}_{4 \text{ places}}$$

STEP **2** Count the number of places between the new decimal point and the original decimal point. The index of the base 10 is the negative value of this number.

Hence $0.000\ 840 = 8.40 \times 10^{-4}$.

▶ *Try It 10!* Express the following numbers in standard form.
(a) 378 000　　　　　　　　(b) 0.000 092

Example 11 Express each of the following as an integer or a decimal.
(a) 4.25×10^5　　　　　(b) 3.17×10^{-6}

Solution (a) $4.25 \times 10^5 = 4.25 \times 100\ 000$
$= 425\ 000$

(b) $3.17 \times 10^{-6} = \dfrac{3.17}{1\ 000\ 000}$
$= 0.000\ 003\ 17$

(a) It can be done by moving the decimal point 5 places to the right.
(b) It can be done by moving the decimal point 6 places to the left.

▶ *Try It 11!* Express each of the following as an integer or a decimal.
(a) 7.92×10^4　　　　　(b) 2.68×10^{-5}

We have special names for some powers of 10. The following table illustrates the commonly used ones.

Powers of 10	Name	SI Prefix	Symbol	Example
10^{-12}	trillionth	pico-	p	1 picolitre = 10^{-12} ℓ
10^{-9}	billionth	nano-	n	1 nanometre = 10^{-9} m
10^{-6}	millionth	micro-	μ	1 microsecond = 10^{-6} s
10^{-3}	thousandth	milli-	m	1 milliampere = 10^{-3} A
10^0	one			
10^3	thousand	kilo-	k	1 kilogram = 10^3 g
10^6	million	mega-	M	1 Megahertz = 10^6 Hz
10^9	billion	giga-	G	1 Gigabyte = 10^9 Bytes
10^{12}	trillion	tera-	T	1 Terajoule = 10^{12} J

The Scale of Things

| Ant
~ 5 mm | Dust mite
~ 200 μm | Red blood cells
~ 2–5 μm | DNA
~ 2–12 nm diameter |

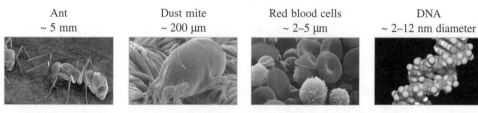

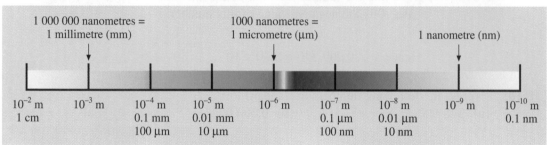

1 000 000 nanometres =
1 millimetre (mm)

1000 nanometres =
1 micrometre (μm)

1 nanometre (nm)

| 10^{-2} m
1 cm | 10^{-3} m | 10^{-4} m
0.1 mm
100 μm | 10^{-5} m
0.01 mm
10 μm | 10^{-6} m | 10^{-7} m
0.1 μm
100 nm | 10^{-8} m
0.01 μm
10 nm | 10^{-9} m | 10^{-10} m
0.1 nm |

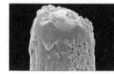

| Point of pin
0.8–1 mm diameter | Micro mechanical device
10–100 μm wide | Nanotube
1–10 nm diameter |

B. Computation

The following examples illustrate the four operations of numbers in standard form.

Example 12 Evaluate the following and express your answers in standard form.
 (a) $4.3 \times 10^4 + 5.2 \times 10^5$
 (b) $9.27 \times 10^{-7} - 1.68 \times 10^{-8}$

Express the smaller number in the form $d \times 10^n$, where 10^n is the same as that of the larger number.
Add the decimal parts.

Solution **(a)** $4.3 \times 10^4 + 5.2 \times 10^5 = 0.43 \times 10^5 + 5.2 \times 10^5$
$= (0.43 + 5.2) \times 10^5$
$= 5.63 \times 10^5$

 (b) $9.27 \times 10^{-7} - 1.68 \times 10^{-8} = 9.27 \times 10^{-7} - 0.168 \times 10^{-7}$
$= (9.27 - 0.168) \times 10^{-7}$
$= 9.102 \times 10^{-7}$

Note: In using a calculator, the key sequences are as follows.

 (a) 4.3 EXP 4 + 5.2 EXP 5 =

 (b) 9.27 EXP +/− 7 − 1.68 EXP +/− 8 =

That means we use the EXP key to enter a number in standard form.

Try It 12! Evaluate the following and express your answers in standard form.
(a) $3.9 \times 10^6 + 4.7 \times 10^7$
(b) $8.25 \times 10^{-13} - 6.01 \times 10^{-14}$

Example 13 Evaluate the following and express your answers in standard form.
(a) $(2.4 \times 10^6) \times (5 \times 10^{-4})$
(b) $(2.34 \times 10^{-5}) \div (1.3 \times 10^7)$

Solution (a) $(2.4 \times 10^6) \times (5 \times 10^{-4}) = (2.4 \times 5) \times (10^6 \times 10^{-4})$
$$= 12 \times 10^{6-4}$$
$$= 12 \times 10^2$$
$$= 1.2 \times 10^3$$

Marvel at the scale of things in our universe!
http://micro.magnet.fsu.edu/ primer/java/scienceopticsu/ powersof10

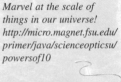

(b) $(2.34 \times 10^{-5}) \div (1.3 \times 10^7) = \dfrac{2.34 \times 10^{-5}}{1.3 \times 10^7}$
$$= \frac{2.34}{1.3} \times \frac{10^{-5}}{10^7}$$
$$= 1.8 \times 10^{-5-7}$$
$$= 1.8 \times 10^{-12}$$

 Try It 13! Evaluate the following and express your answers in standard form.
(a) $(9.5 \times 10^{13}) \times (4 \times 10^{-6})$
(b) $(2.38 \times 10^{-5}) \div (1.4 \times 10^4)$

Example 14 The storage capacity of a computer hard disk is 160 GB. If the size of each document is 5 kB, how many documents can be stored in the hard disk? Give your answer in standard form.
($1 \text{ GB} = 1 \times 10^9 \text{ B}$; $1 \text{ kB} = 1 \times 10^3 \text{ B}$)

Solution $160 \text{ GB} = 160 \times 10^9$ bytes
$5 \text{ kB} = 5 \times 10^3$ bytes

$\therefore$ number of documents that can be stored $= \dfrac{160 \times 10^9}{5 \times 10^3}$
$$= 32 \times 10^6$$
$$= 3.2 \times 10^7$$

 Try It 14! The storage capacity of a memory card in a digital camera is 512 MB. Suppose each digital photo takes up 640 kB. How many photos can be stored on the memory card?

C. Rounding and Truncation Errors in a Calculator

Class Activity 4

1. Let $Y = 7 \times 10^{10} + 7 \times 10^5 + 7$.

   (a) Find the value of Y by expressing each number in integer form, without using a calculator.

Number	Integer Form
7×10^{10}	70 000 000 000
7×10^5	700 000
7 +	7

   $Y \quad = \quad$ ▨

   (b) Find the value of Y using a calculator.

   (c) Compare the answers in **(a)** and **(b)**. Are they the same?

   (d) Compare your answer in **(b)** with those of your classmates who use different models of calculators. Do you get the same answer as they?

2. Consider the number 4×10^{12}.

   (a) Enter the number in your calculator.

   Find $\sqrt{\sqrt{\sqrt{4 \times 10^{12}}}}$.

   Square the answer 3 times.
   Then subtract 4×10^{12} from the answer displayed in the calculator.
   Write down the final answer displayed in the calculator.

   (b) Enter the number in your calculator again.

   Find $\sqrt{\sqrt{\sqrt{\sqrt{\sqrt{\sqrt{4 \times 10^{12}}}}}}}$.

   Square the answer 6 times.
   Then subtract 4×10^{12} from the answer displayed in the calculator.
   Write down the final answer displayed in the calculator.

   (c) What are the expected answers in **(a)** and **(b)**?

   (d) Comment on the answers obtained in **(a)** and **(b)**.

From Class Activity 4, we see that calculations using a calculator may not yield exact answers. This is due to the rounding and truncation errors at each stage of the calculation by the calculator. We must therefore check the answers obtained from a calculator.

Exercise 1.4

Basic Practice

1. Express the following numbers in standard form.
   (a) 83 700
   (b) 720 000
   (c) 96 200 000
   (d) 1 450 000 000
   (e) 0.000 16
   (f) 0.000 028
   (g) 0.000 009 5
   (h) 0.000 000 030

2. Express the following numbers as integers.
   (a) 9.8×10^3
   (b) 5×10^4
   (c) 7.23×10^6
   (d) 1.06×10^8

3. Express the following numbers as decimals.
   (a) 4×10^{-3}
   (b) 3.6×10^{-5}
   (c) 1.58×10^{-6}
   (d) 2.07×10^{-10}

4. Evaluate the following without using a calculator and express your answers in standard form.
   (a) $3.6 \times 10^4 + 4.7 \times 10^5$
   (b) $6.8 \times 10^{-9} + 9 \times 10^{-7}$
   (c) $4 \times 10^6 - 9.8 \times 10^5$
   (d) $5.4 \times 10^{-11} - 6.6 \times 10^{-12}$
   (e) $(5 \times 10^6) \times (3 \times 10^8)$
   (f) $(4 \times 10^{-5}) \times (1.7 \times 10^9)$
   (g) $(2 \times 10^{-3}) \div (8 \times 10^{-7})$
   (h) $(3.4 \times 10^{-4}) \div (1.7 \times 10^5)$

Further Practice

5. Evaluate the following without using a calculator and express your answers in standard form.
   (a) $(1.3 \times 10^7)^2$
   (b) $(5 \times 10^{-6})^3$
   (c) $\sqrt{1.96 \times 10^8}$
   (d) $\sqrt[3]{2.16 \times 10^{-10}}$
   (e) $\dfrac{(2 \times 10^{-5}) \times (6 \times 10^7)}{4 \times 10^{-8}}$
   (f) $\dfrac{8 \times 10^{-4} + 1 \times 10^{-5}}{5 \times 10^6 - 5 \times 10^5}$

Maths@Work

6. In the year 2005, the population in Singapore was about 4.4×10^6. If each person, on average, consumed 0.4 kg of meat a day, how many kilograms of meat were consumed in Singapore in a day in 2005?

7. An atom of an element consists of protons, neutrons and electrons. An electron has a mass 5×10^{-4} times the mass of a proton. The mass of an electron is $9.109\ 56 \times 10^{-31}$ kg. Find the mass of a proton, expressing your answer in standard form correct to 3 significant figures.

8. (a) The equatorial radius of the Earth is the distance from the centre of the Earth to the equator. It is about 6378.5 km. Find the length of the equator in metres, expressing your answer in standard form.

   (b) The speed of light in air is 3×10^8 m/s. Find the time taken for a light beam to travel a distance equal to the length of the equator. Give your answer correct to 3 significant figures.

equator

Brainworks

9. List some units of measurement in daily life that use the SI prefixes pico-, nano-, micro-, mega-, giga-, tera-, etc.

10. Provide an example that shows the rounding and truncation errors in a calculator.

1.5 Comparing Indices

We can use the following fact to find an unknown index.

> If $a^x = a^y$, where $a > 0$ and $a \neq 1$, then $x = y$.

Example 15 Find the value of x if $2^x = 64$.

Solution
$$2^x = 64$$
$$2^x = 2^6 \qquad \text{Express 64 as a power of 2.}$$
$$\therefore \quad x = 6 \qquad \text{Equate the indices on both sides.}$$

▶ *Try It 15!* Find the value of x if $3^x = 243$.

Exercise 1.5

Basic Practice

1. Solve the following equations.
    (a) $2^x = 32$ (b) $3^x = 729$
    (c) $4^x = 64$ (d) $7^x = 343$

Further Practice

2. Solve the following equations.
    (a) $7^{x+2} = 343$ (b) $2^{3x+1} = 16$
    (c) $5^{9-x} = 625$ (d) $3^x = \dfrac{1}{243}$

Maths@Work

3. The number of bacteria in a colony is 2^{t+1}, where t is the number of hours after the first observation. After how many hours will there be 1024 bacteria?

4. Consider the sequence 729, 243, 81, 27, ...
    (a) Write down the 5th and 6th terms of the sequence.
    (b) Express the nth term of the sequence in terms of n.
    (c) If the nth term of the sequence is $\dfrac{1}{2187}$, find the value of n.

Brainworks

5. The solution of the equation $4^x = 2^n$ is an integer x. Find two possible values of the constant n.

Definition of a^n

1. When n is a positive integer,

   (a) $a^n = \underbrace{a \times a \times a \ldots \times a}_{n \text{ factors}}$;

   (b) $a^{-n} = \dfrac{1}{a^n}$, if $a \neq 0$;

   (c) $a^{\frac{1}{n}} = \sqrt[n]{a}$, if $a > 0$.

2. $a^0 = 1$, if $a \neq 0$.

3. When $a > 0$, m and n are integers, and $n > 0$, $a^{\frac{m}{n}} = (\sqrt[n]{a})^m$.

Laws of Indices

Let a and b be real numbers, and m and n be rational numbers.

1. $a^m \times a^n = a^{m+n}$

2. $a^m \div a^n = a^{m-n}$

3. $(a^m)^n = a^{mn}$

4. $(ab)^n = a^n b^n$

5. $\left(\dfrac{a}{b}\right)^n = \dfrac{a^n}{b^n}$, if $b \neq 0$

Standard Form

The standard form of a number is

$$A \times 10^n,$$

where $1 \leqslant A < 10$ and n is an integer.

Comparing Indices

If $a^x = a^y$, where $a > 0$ and $a \neq 1$, then $x = y$.

Revision Exercise 1

1. Simplify the following, expressing your answers with positive indices.
   (a) $(x^3y)(x^4y^2)$
   (b) $(a^5b^6) \div (a^3b^8)$

   (c) $(2a^3b^4)^3$
   (d) $\dfrac{(-2p^3q^2)^2}{(4p^2q^5)^3}$

2. Evaluate the following.
   (a) $10^{-2} + 10^0 + 10^2$
   (b) $3^{-1} - 4^{-2}$

   (c) $\left(\dfrac{4}{5}\right)^{-3}$
   (d) $\left(\dfrac{2}{3}\right)^3 \div \left(\dfrac{9}{4}\right)^{-2}$

3. Simplify the following, expressing your answers with positive indices.
   (a) $(x^3y^{-1})(x^{-4}y^5)$
   (b) $(-2x^4y^3)^0(-3x^{-4}y^5)^{-2}$

   (c) $\dfrac{(6p^2q^{-3})^5}{(-3pq^{-5})^3}$
   (d) $\left(\dfrac{x^4}{y^{-2}}\right)^3 \div \left(\dfrac{x^{-2}}{y^3}\right)^4$

4. Evaluate the following.

   (a) $\sqrt[4]{1296}$
   (b) $256^{\frac{3}{2}}$

   (c) $128^{-\frac{4}{7}}$
   (d) $1000^{-\frac{2}{3}}$

5. Simplify the following, expressing your answers with positive indices.

   (a) $\sqrt[3]{a^2} \div \sqrt{a^5}$
   (b) $(8a)^{-\frac{1}{3}} \times \sqrt[4]{\dfrac{81}{a^3}}$

   (c) $(m^{-1}n^{\frac{3}{2}})^4(m^{-2}n^{-\frac{4}{3}})^{-\frac{1}{2}}$
   (d) $(a^{\frac{1}{2}} + a^{-\frac{1}{2}})(a^{\frac{1}{2}} - a^{-\frac{1}{2}})$

6. Let $x = 9\ 230\ 000$, $y = 471\ 000$ and $z = 0.000\ 005$.
   (a) Express x, y and z in standard form.
   (b) Find the values of the following, expressing your answers in standard form.
       (i) $x + y$
       (ii) xz

       (iii) z^3
       (iv) $\dfrac{y}{z}$

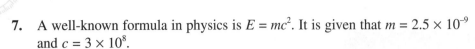

7. A well-known formula in physics is $E = mc^2$. It is given that $m = 2.5 \times 10^{-9}$ and $c = 3 \times 10^8$.

   (a) Express m as a decimal.

   (b) Express c as an integer.

   (c) Find the value of E, expressing your answer

       (i) in standard form,   (ii) as an integer.

8. (a) Find the number of seconds in a day.

   (b) Suppose there are 365.24 days in a year. Find the number of seconds in a year correct to 3 significant figures, expressing your answer in standard form.

   (c) Sulin just turned 15 years old. How many seconds has she been living? Give your answer in standard form, correct to 3 significant figures.

9. Solve the following equations.

   (a) $2^x = 512$ (b) $5^{2x+1} = 625$

10. (a) Write down, correct to the nearest integer, the value of $\sqrt{896}$.   [1]

    (b) In 1998 there were 4.9×10^7 people living in England and of these 9.3×10^6 were under 16 years of age.

    Find the number of people who were 16 or over. Give your answer in standard form.   [2]

    NP1/2000/9

11. (a) A pile of 1500 sheets of paper is 6 cm high. Find the thickness of one sheet of paper

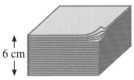

6 cm

    (i) in centimetres, giving your answer as a decimal,   [1]

    (ii) in metres, giving your answer in standard form.   [1]

    (b) Each sheet of paper is 30 cm long and 20 cm wide.

    Find the total surface area of both sides of one sheet of paper, giving your answer in square metres.   [1]

    NP1/2001/12

12. (a) On a journey, a cyclist travelled 1 kilometre in x minutes.

    On a second journey, the cyclist travelled for y hours at the same average speed as on the first journey.

    Find an expression, in terms of x and y, for the number of kilometres he travelled on the second journey.   [1]

    (b) $\dfrac{t \times t^3}{\sqrt{t}} = t^n$.

    Find the value of n.   [1]

    NP1/2002/6

13. The population of Europe is approximately 7.0×10^8.
    The population of Asia is approximately 3.5×10^9.
    The mean mass of the population of Europe is approximately 62 kg.
    (a) Giving your answers in standard form, estimate
        (i) the total mass of the population of Europe, [1]
        (ii) how many more people live in Asia than in Europe. [1]
    (b) Express the population of Europe as a percentage of the population of Asia. [1]

    NP1/2002/12

14. (a) Write down the following numbers in order of size starting with the smallest
        $$-0.29, -1.5, 0, -0.3, -4.$$ [1]
    (b) The thickness of a sheet of paper is 8×10^{-4} cm. Find the thickness of two sheets of paper, giving your answer in standard form. [1]

    NP1/2003/8

15. Find a, b and c when
    (a) $3^a \div 3^5 = 27$, [1]
    (b) $125^b = 5$, [1]
    (c) $10^c = 0.001$. [1]

    NP1/2003/12

16. (a) Express $\dfrac{17}{40}$ as a percentage. [1]

    (b) Evaluate $\left(\dfrac{1}{3}\right)^{-2}$. [1]

    NP1/2004/6

17. An atom of helium has a mass of 6.8×10^{-27} kilograms.
    (a) Express this mass in grams.
        Give your answer in standard form. [1]
    (b) A room contains 9×10^{22} atoms of helium.
        Find the mass of helium in the room.
        Give your answer in grams as a normal decimal number. [2]

    NP1/2004/12

Nanometre Technology

Even small things can affect our lives very much. In recent years, a new branch of science, called *nanometre technology* or *nano-technology*, has allowed scientists to make molecular changes to the structure of certain substances. This technology can be applied, for instance, to the production of computer chips, the development of nanoscale drug delivery systems and implantation medicine.

Research and write a brief report on this technology and its possible applications.

Write In Your Journal

Why is standard form convenient for writing extremely large or small numbers? Does standard form help you to understand why our standard number system is called a **base 10** system?

2 More About Quadratic Equations

Quadratic equations are necessary to understand the mechanics of motion. If the distance, s metres, travelled by a car in time t seconds is given by $s = 3t^2 + 4t$, do you know how long it takes the car to travel 100 m?

Let's learn to...

- solve quadratic equations by factorisation, completing the square method, quadratic formula and graphical method
- solve fractional equations that can be transformed to quadratic equations
- apply quadratic equations to solve everyday problems

2.1 Factorisation Method

An equation that can be written in the form $ax^2 + bx + c = 0$, where a, b and c are real numbers and $a \neq 0$, is called a **quadratic equation**. There are several methods for solving a quadratic equation. Let us first revise the factorisation method that we have learnt in Secondary 2.

Example 1   Solve the equation $3x^2 + 5x - 2 = 0$.

Solution
$$3x^2 + 5x - 2 = 0$$
$$(3x - 1)(x + 2) = 0 \qquad \text{Factorise the LHS.}$$
$$\therefore \qquad 3x - 1 = 0 \quad \text{or} \quad x + 2 = 0$$
$$x = \frac{1}{3} \quad \text{or} \qquad x = -2$$

$$
\begin{array}{c|c}
3x & -1 & -x \\
x & +2 & +6x \\
\hline
3x^2 & -2 & 5x
\end{array}
$$

▶ *Try It 1!*   Solve the equation $2x^2 + 9x - 5 = 0$.

Example 2   Solve the equation $(4x + 1)(x - 3) = 9x - 28$.

Solution
$$(4x + 1)(x - 3) = 9x - 28$$
$$4x^2 - 11x - 3 = 9x - 28 \qquad \text{Expand the LHS.}$$
$$4x^2 - 20x + 25 = 0 \qquad \text{Move all the terms to the LHS.}$$
$$(2x - 5)^2 = 0 \qquad \text{Factorise the LHS.}$$
$$\therefore \qquad 2x - 5 = 0 \quad \text{or} \quad 2x - 5 = 0$$
$$x = \frac{5}{2} \qquad \text{Both factors are the same, therefore the roots are equal.}$$

$$
\begin{array}{c|c}
2x & -5 & -10x \\
2x & -5 & -10x \\
\hline
4x^2 & +25 & -20x
\end{array}
$$

or use
$$a^2 - 2ab + b^2 = (a - b)^2$$
to factorise.

▶ *Try It 2!*   Solve the equation $(9x - 1)(x - 2) = -7x - 2$.

Example 3   Solve the equation $4x(3x + 5) = 7(3x + 5)$.

Solution
$$4x(3x + 5) = 7(3x + 5)$$
$$4x(3x + 5) - 7(3x + 5) = 0$$
$$(4x - 7)(3x + 5) = 0$$
$$4x - 7 = 0 \quad \text{or} \quad 3x + 5 = 0$$
$$x = \frac{7}{4} \quad \text{or} \qquad x = -\frac{5}{3}$$

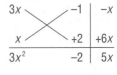

Equal roots are also known as double roots or repeated roots.

Remark

Note: 1.   This equation can be solved by expanding both sides first. However, factors can be obtained readily by using the above method since $3x + 5$ is a common factor on both sides.

   2.   We cannot cancel the factor $3x + 5$ from both sides of the given equation. Otherwise, we lose the root $x = -\frac{5}{3}$.

▶ *Try It 3!*   Solve the equation $2x(5x + 3) = 9(5x + 3)$.

Exercise 2.1

Basic Practice

1. Solve the following equations.
   (a) $x^2 - 4x + 3 = 0$
   (b) $x^2 - 2x - 8 = 0$
   (c) $2x^2 - 3x + 1 = 0$
   (d) $15x^2 + 8x + 1 = 0$
   (e) $2x^2 + x - 6 = 0$
   (f) $3x^2 - 2x - 5 = 0$
   (g) $8x^2 + 10x + 3 = 0$
   (h) $14x^2 - 29x = 15$

Further Practice

2. Solve the following equations.
   (a) $x^2 - 2x = 5x - 12$
   (b) $x(x + 11) = 2(x + 5)$
   (c) $3x(2x + 5) = 4(2x + 5)$
   (d) $36 - 25x^2 = 0$
   (e) $(7x + 2)(2x - 3) = 5x - 6$
   (f) $(x + 1)^2 = 9(x + 1)$
   (g) $(2x - 1)^2 - 4(2x - 1) - 5 = 0$
   (h) $2(3x + 4)^2 - 5(3x + 4) + 3 = 0$

Maths@Work

3. The sum of the areas of two squares is 269 cm². The side
   of one square is 3 cm longer than that of the other square.
   Find the length of a side of the smaller square.

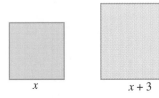

4. The three sides of a right-angled triangle are $(x + 2)$ cm,
   $(2x + 3)$ cm and $(3x - 1)$ cm. Find the value of x.

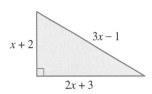

Brainworks

5. Sumin solved the equation $3x(x + 4) = x(x + 1)$ as follows. Is her solution
   correct? Explain your answer.

$$3x(x + 4) = x(x + 1)$$
$$3(x + 4) = x + 1$$
$$3x + 12 = x + 1$$
$$2x = -11$$
$$\therefore \quad x = -\frac{11}{2}$$

6. Peter solved the equation $(5x - 2)^2 = (2x + 1)^2$ as follows. Is his solution correct? Explain your answer.

> $$(5x - 2)^2 = (2x + 1)^2$$
>
> Taking square roots of both sides,
>
> $$5x - 2 = 2x + 1$$
> $$3x = 3$$
> $$\therefore \quad x = 1.$$

2.2 Graphical Method

Some quadratic equations, such as $x^2 - x - 3 = 0$, cannot be solved by the factorisation method. An alternative way is to solve these equations graphically, that is, by drawing their corresponding quadratic graphs.

Example 4   Solve the equation $x^2 - x - 3 = 0$ graphically, by drawing the graph of $y = x^2 - x - 3$ for $-3 \leqslant x \leqslant 3$.

Solution   First, construct a table of values of $y = x^2 - x - 3$ for $-3 \leqslant x \leqslant 3$. Then draw the graph.

x	-3	-2	-1	0	1	2	3
y	9	3	-1	-3	-3	-1	3

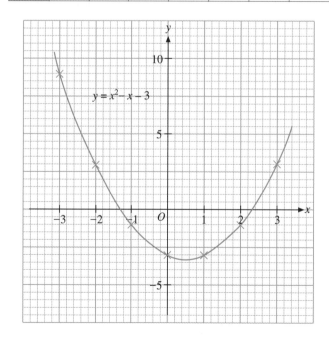

When the graph of $y = x^2 - x - 3$ cuts the x-axis, we have $y = 0$.
That means $x^2 - x - 3 = 0$.

∴ the roots of the equation $x^2 - x - 3 = 0$ are the x-coordinates of the points of intersection of the graph of $y = x^2 - x - 3$ and the x-axis.

Hence the required roots are

$x = -1.3$ or $x = 2.3$ (correct to one decimal place).

▶ *Try It 4!*   Solve the equation $x^2 + x - 4 = 0$ graphically for $-3 \leqslant x \leqslant 3$.
(Copy and complete the following table. Draw the graph of $y = x^2 + x - 4$. Use a scale of 1 cm to 1 unit on the x-axis and a scale of 2 cm to 5 units on the y-axis.)

x	−3	−2	−1	0	1	2	3
$y = x^2 + x - 4$							

Example 5   Solve the equation $x^2 - 2x + 1 = 0$ graphically, by drawing the graph of $y = x^2 - 2x + 1$ for $-2 \leqslant x \leqslant 4$.

Solution   Draw the graph of $y = x^2 - 2x + 1$.

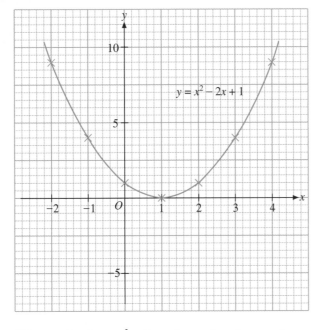

x	−2	−1	0	1	2	3	4
y	9	4	1	0	1	4	9

The graph of $y = x^2 - 2x + 1$ touches the x-axis at $x = 1$ only.
∴ the root of the equation $x^2 - 2x + 1 = 0$ is

$x = 1$.   ⟶   The root is repeated.

Note: When the graph of $y = ax^2 + bx + c$ touches the x-axis at one point only, the equation $ax^2 + bx + c = 0$ has equal or repeated roots.

▶ *Try It 5!* Solve the equation $x^2 + 4x + 4 = 0$ graphically for $-5 \leqslant x \leqslant 1$. (Copy and complete the following table. Draw the graph of $y = x^2 + 4x + 4$. Use a scale of 1 cm to 1 unit on the x-axis and a scale of 2 cm to 5 units on the y-axis.)

x	−5	−4	−3	−2	−1	0	1
$y = x^2 + 4x + 4$							

Example 6 Solve the equation $2x^2 - 5x + 7 = 0$ graphically, by drawing the graph of $y = 2x^2 - 5x + 7$ for $-1 \leqslant x \leqslant 4$.

Solution

x	−1	0	1	2	3	4
$y = 2x^2 - 5x + 7$	14	7	4	5	10	19

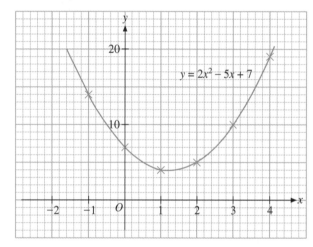

The graph of $y = 2x^2 - 5x + 7$ does not cut the x-axis.
∴ there is no value of x that makes $2x^2 - 5x + 7 = 0$.

Hence the equation $2x^2 - 5x + 7 = 0$ has **no real roots**.

We can also say, no real number x satisfies $2x^2 - 5x + 7 = 0$.

Note: An equation $ax^2 + bx + c = 0$ has no real roots if the graph of $y = ax^2 + bx + c$ does not cut the x-axis.

▶ *Try It 6!* Solve the equation $x^2 - x + 3 = 0$ graphically for $-2 \leqslant x \leqslant 3$. (Copy and complete the following table. Draw the graph of $y = x^2 - x + 3$. Use a scale of 1 cm to 1 unit on the x-axis and a scale of 2 cm to 5 units on the y-axis.)

x	−2	−1	0	1	2	3
$y = x^2 - x + 3$						

Exercise 2.2

Basic Practice

1. **(a)** Copy and complete the following table.

x	–3	–2	–1	0	1	2	3
$y = x^2 - 3$							

    (b) Draw the graph of $y = x^2 - 3$ for $-3 \leqslant x \leqslant 3$.
    (c) Hence solve the equation $x^2 - 3 = 0$ graphically.

2. **(a)** Copy and complete the following table.

x	–1	0	1	2	3	4	5
$y = x^2 - 4x + 4$							

    (b) Draw the graph of $y = x^2 - 4x + 4$ for $-1 \leqslant x \leqslant 5$.
    (c) Hence solve the equation $x^2 - 4x + 4 = 0$ graphically.

3. **(a)** Copy and complete the following table.

x	–3	–2	–1	0	1	2
$y = x^2 + x + 2$						

    (b) Draw the graph of $y = x^2 + x + 2$ for $-3 \leqslant x \leqslant 2$.
    (c) Hence solve the equation $x^2 + x + 2 = 0$ graphically.

Further Practice

4. **(a)** Draw the graph of $y = x^2 - 2x - 3$ for $-2 \leqslant x \leqslant 4$.
    (b) Hence solve the equation $x^2 - 2x - 3 = 0$ graphically.

5. **(a)** Draw the graph of $y = 2x^2 + 5x - 1$ for $-3 \leqslant x \leqslant 2$.
    (b) Hence solve the equation $2x^2 + 5x - 1 = 0$ graphically.

6. **(a)** Draw the graph of $y = 3x^2 - 2x + 4$ for $-2 \leqslant x \leqslant 3$.
    (b) Hence solve the equation $3x^2 - 2x + 4 = 0$ graphically.

7. A dolphin leaped out of the sea, dived back into the sea and then leaped out again. It was observed that the height, h metres, of the dolphin's leap above the sea level at time t seconds, is given by $h = t^2 - 5t + 1$ for $0 \leqslant t \leqslant 5$.

(a) Draw the graph of $h = t^2 - 5t + 1$ for $0 \leqslant t \leqslant 5$.

(b) Determine graphically the times at which the dolphin was at sea level.

Brainworks

8. Can the quadratic equation $6 - 2x - x^2 = 0$ be solved by the graphical method? If so, illustrate the steps and find the roots.

9. (a) Draw the graph of $y = x^2 - 3x$ for $-2 \leqslant x \leqslant 5$.

(b) Solve graphically the equation $x^2 - 3x = 0$.

(c) Can you use the graph in (a) to solve the equation $x^2 - 3x - 4 = 0$ without drawing another quadratic graph? If so, illustrate your method and find the roots of the equation.

(*Hint*: You may consider adding the graph of a straight line on the same grid.)

2.3 Completing The Square Method

We can use the graphical method to solve any quadratic equation. The drawbacks are it takes time to draw the graph and the degree of accuracy is limited. Let us now learn an algebraic method that involves adding a term to the expression $x^2 + bx$ to make it a perfect square in order to solve the given quadratic equation. In other words, we need to find a term c, which, when added to $x^2 + bx$, will make $x^2 + bx + c$ a perfect square, $(x + p)^2$, for some p.

Class Activity 1

Suppose $x^2 + bx + c = (x + p)^2$.

1. Copy and complete the following table.

p	$(x + p)^2$	$x^2 + bx + c$	b	c
5	$(x + 5)^2$	$x^2 + 10x + 25$	10	25
3				
−7				
$-\dfrac{1}{2}$				
		$x^2 + 2x + 1$		
		$x^2 - 4x + 4$		
			12	
			−8	
			3	
			−5	

$(x + a)^2 = x^2 + 2ax + a^2$
$(x - a)^2 = x^2 - 2ax + a^2$

Recall

2. The figure is made up of a square and two identical rectangles.
   (a) Find Area I + Area II + Area III.

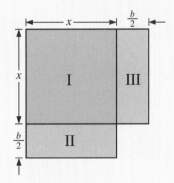

   (b) To make the figure a square, what shape should be added to it?

3. What is the area of the shape obtained in **2(b)**?

The use of an algorithmic approach, which eventually gave rise to quadratic equations, started around 3000 BC with the Babylonians. One of its uses was for calculating the amount of crops that the farmers had to pay the taxmen.

MathsBits

In general, the expression $x^2 + bx$ becomes a perfect square when $\left(\frac{b}{2}\right)^2$ is added to it.

Thus,

$$x^2 + bx + \left(\frac{b}{2}\right)^2 = \left(x + \frac{b}{2}\right)^2.$$

Solving a quadratic equation using this approach is called the **completing the square method**.

Example 7   Solve the equation $x^2 + 6x - 7 = 0$ by the completing the square method.

Solution

$$x^2 + 6x - 7 = 0$$
$$x^2 + 6x = 7 \qquad \text{Move the constant term to the RHS.}$$
$$x^2 + 6x + \left(\frac{6}{2}\right)^2 = 7 + \left(\frac{6}{2}\right)^2 \qquad \text{Add } \left(\frac{6}{2}\right)^2 \text{ to both sides.}$$
$$x^2 + 6x + 3^2 = 7 + 3^2 \qquad \text{Write the LHS as a perfect square.}$$
$$(x + 3)^2 = 16 \qquad \text{Take the square root of both sides.}$$
$$\therefore \qquad x + 3 = \pm\sqrt{16}$$
$$x + 3 = 4 \quad \text{or} \quad x + 3 = -4$$
$$\therefore \qquad x = 1 \quad \text{or} \qquad x = -7$$

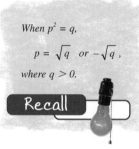

When $p^2 = q$,

$$p = \sqrt{q} \ \text{ or } \ -\sqrt{q},$$

where $q > 0$.

Recall

Note: The equation $x^2 + 6x - 7 = 0$ can be solved by the factorisation method.

▶ *Try It 7!*   Solve the equation $x^2 + 2x - 15 = 0$ by the completing the square method.

Example 8   Solve the equation $x^2 - x - 3 = 0$ by the completing the square method.

Solution

$$x^2 - x - 3 = 0$$
$$x^2 - x = 3 \qquad\qquad b = -1$$
$$x^2 - x + \left(-\frac{1}{2}\right)^2 = 3 + \left(-\frac{1}{2}\right)^2 \qquad \left(\frac{b}{2}\right)^2 = \left(-\frac{1}{2}\right)^2$$
$$\left(x - \frac{1}{2}\right)^2 = \frac{13}{4}$$
$$x - \frac{1}{2} = \pm\sqrt{\frac{13}{4}}$$
$$\therefore \qquad x - \frac{1}{2} = -\frac{\sqrt{13}}{2} \qquad \text{or} \quad x - \frac{1}{2} = \frac{\sqrt{13}}{2}$$
$$x = \frac{1}{2} - \frac{\sqrt{13}}{2} \quad \text{or} \quad x = \frac{1}{2} + \frac{\sqrt{13}}{2}$$
$$\therefore \qquad x = -1.30 \qquad \text{or} \quad x = 2.30 \quad \text{(correct to 3 sig. fig.)}$$

Compare this solution with that in Example 4 for the same equation.

*A number in the form $a + b\sqrt{n}$, is called a **number in surd form**, where a and b are integers or fractions, $b \neq 0$, n is a positive integer and $\sqrt{n}$ is not an integer.*

▶ *Try It 8!*   Solve the equation $x^2 - 3x - 5 = 0$ by the completing the square method.

Exercise 2.3

Basic Practice

1. Find the constant term that must be added to each of the following expressions to make it a perfect square.
   (a) $x^2 + 2x$
   (b) $x^2 - 4x$
   (c) $x^2 - 8x$
   (d) $x^2 + 7x$
   (e) $x^2 + x$
   (f) $x^2 - 11x$

2. Solve the following equations, giving your answers correct to 3 significant figures.
   (a) $(x - 1)^2 = 25$
   (b) $(x + 3)^2 = 49$
   (c) $\left(x + \dfrac{1}{2}\right)^2 = 1$
   (d) $\left(x - \dfrac{5}{2}\right)^2 = \dfrac{9}{4}$
   (e) $(x + 4)^2 = 7$
   (f) $(x - 3)^2 = 10$

3. Solve the following equations by the completing the square method, giving your answers correct to 3 significant figures.
   (a) $x^2 + 4x + 3 = 0$
   (b) $x^2 - 8x + 12 = 0$
   (c) $x^2 - 3x + 1 = 0$
   (d) $x^2 + 5x - 2 = 0$

4. Solve the following equations by the completing the square method, giving your answers correct to 2 decimal places.
   (a) $x^2 - 12x + 36 = 0$
   (b) $x^2 - 4x - 21 = 0$
   (c) $x^2 + 7x - 5 = 0$
   (d) $x^2 - x - 1 = 0$

Further Practice

5. Solve the following equations by the completing the square method, giving your answers correct to 3 significant figures.
   (a) $x^2 + 18x = 13$
   (b) $x(x - 5) = 7(x + 1)$
   (c) $(x - 1)(x + 8) = 1 - 6x$
   (d) $(x - 4)^2 = 9x$

Maths@Work

6. The cost of a square artwork of length x cm is $\$(x^2 + 4x)$. If an artwork costs $300, what is its length?

Brainworks

7. Find a quadratic equation whose roots are $2 - \sqrt{3}$ and $2 + \sqrt{3}$.

8. What can you say about the roots of the equation $(x - 1)^2 = -1$?

2.4 Quadratic Formula

We can use the completing the square method to find yet another method for solving the quadratic equation $ax^2 + bx + c = 0$.

$$ax^2 + bx + c = 0$$

$$x^2 + \frac{b}{a}x + \frac{c}{a} = 0 \qquad \text{Divide each term by } a \text{ so that the coefficient of } x^2 \text{ is 1.}$$

$$x^2 + \frac{b}{a}x = -\frac{c}{a} \qquad \text{Move } \frac{c}{a} \text{ to the RHS.}$$

$$x^2 + \frac{b}{a}x + \left(\frac{b}{2a}\right)^2 = -\frac{c}{a} + \left(\frac{b}{2a}\right)^2 \qquad \text{Add } \left(\frac{b}{2a}\right)^2 \text{ to both sides.}$$

$$\left(x + \frac{b}{2a}\right)^2 = \frac{b^2 - 4ac}{4a^2} \qquad \text{Factorise the LHS and simplify the RHS.}$$

$$x + \frac{b}{2a} = \pm\sqrt{\frac{b^2 - 4ac}{4a^2}} \qquad \text{Take the square root of both sides.}$$

$$\therefore \quad x = -\frac{b}{2a} - \frac{\sqrt{b^2 - 4ac}}{2a} \quad \text{or} \quad x = -\frac{b}{2a} + \frac{\sqrt{b^2 - 4ac}}{2a}$$

Hence, we have the *quadratic formula as follows*:

The roots of $ax^2 + bx + c = 0$ are $x = \dfrac{-b \pm \sqrt{b^2 - 4ac}}{2a}$.

Explore the applet on the quadratic formula at http://www.univie.ac.at/ future.media/moe/galerie/ gleich/gleich.html under Applet: Quadratic equations 1.

Example 9 Solve the equation $3x^2 + 5x - 1 = 0$, giving your answers correct to 3 decimal places.

Solution For the equation $3x^2 + 5x - 1 = 0$,

$$a = 3, \ b = 5 \text{ and } c = -1.$$

$$\therefore \ x = \frac{-b \pm \sqrt{b^2 - 4ac}}{2a}$$

$$= \frac{-5 \pm \sqrt{5^2 - 4(3)(-1)}}{2(3)}$$

$$= \frac{-5 \pm \sqrt{37}}{6}$$

$$\therefore \ x = -1.847 \quad \text{or} \quad x = 0.180 \quad \text{(correct to 3 decimal places)}$$

▶ *Try It* **9!** Solve the equation $4x^2 + 7x - 3 = 0$, giving your answers correct to 3 decimal places.

Example 10   Solve the equation $(2x + 3)(2x + 9) = 2(2x + 1)$ by using the quadratic formula.

Solution   We first convert the equation into the form $ax^2 + bx + c = 0$.

$$(2x + 3)(2x + 9) = 2(2x + 1)$$
$$4x^2 + 24x + 27 = 4x + 2$$
$$4x^2 + 20x + 25 = 0$$

i.e. $a = 4$, $b = 20$ and $c = 25$.

$$\therefore \qquad x = \frac{-20 \pm \sqrt{20^2 - 4(4)(25)}}{2(4)}$$

$$= \frac{-20 \pm 0}{8}$$

$$= -\frac{5}{2}$$

Note: This equation has equal roots.

Discuss

What do you observe about the value of $b^2 - 4ac$, if the equation $ax^2 + bx + c = 0$ has real and equal roots?

▶ *Try It 10!*   Solve the equation $(9x + 5)(x + 2) = -x - 6$ by using the quadratic formula.

Example 11   Solve the equation $2x^2 + 7 = 3x$.

Solution
$$2x^2 + 7 = 3x$$
$$2x^2 - 3x + 7 = 0$$

Here $a = 2$, $b = -3$ and $c = 7$.

$$\therefore \qquad x = \frac{-(-3) \pm \sqrt{(-3)^2 - 4(2)(7)}}{2(2)}$$

$$= \frac{3 \pm \sqrt{-47}}{4}$$

But $\sqrt{-47}$ is not a real number.

∴ the equation has **no real roots**.

Discuss

If an equation $ax^2 + bx + c = 0$ does not have real roots, what can you say about the sign of $b^2 - 4ac$?

Note: When you enter $\sqrt{}$ $+/-$ 47 into your calculator and press $=$, you will get an error message.

▶ *Try It 11!*   Solve the equation $3x^2 + 11 = 5x$.

You have now learnt four methods of solving quadratic equations. Which of these four methods could always be used to solve any quadratic equation?

Exercise 2.4

Basic Practice

1. Solve the following equations by using the quadratic formula, giving your answers correct to 3 decimal places.
   - **(a)** $x^2 - 12x + 36 = 0$
   - **(b)** $2x^2 + 6x + 1 = 0$
   - **(c)** $3x^2 - 2x - 5 = 0$
   - **(d)** $5x^2 - x + 4 = 0$
   - **(e)** $7x^2 + x - 2 = 0$
   - **(f)** $8x^2 + 9 = 0$

Further Practice

2. Solve the following equations by using the quadratic formula, giving your answers correct to 3 significant figures.
   - **(a)** $2x(x - 2) = x + 3$
   - **(b)** $(4x + 7)(x - 1) = 3x + 2$
   - **(c)** $(3x - 2)^2 + 7 = 0$
   - **(d)** $x(1 - 2x) + 9 = 0$

3. Solve the following equations by using any method.
   - **(a)** $(x - 2)(x + 1) = 8$
   - **(b)** $3x^2 - 4 = 7x$
   - **(c)** $(x - 2)(x + 2) = 4(x - 2)$
   - **(d)** $5x(x + 1) = 3(x - 2)$

Maths@Work

4. A ball is thrown from the top of a building. Its vertical distance, h metres, from the ground after time t seconds, is given by $h = 50 + 10t - 5t^2$.
   - **(a)** Find the height of the building.
   - **(b)** When is the ball at the same level as the top of the building again?
   - **(c)** When does the ball reach the ground?
   - **(d)** When is the ball 30 m above the ground?

Brainworks

5. **(a)** Find the number of roots that can be obtained from the quadratic equation $ax^2 + bx + c = 0$.
   (b) How can you determine its number of roots without actually solving it?

2.5 Fractional Equations

When an equation contains unknown(s) in the denominator of one or more of its fractional expressions, it is called a **fractional equation**. Some fractional equations can be solved by transforming them into quadratic equations.

Example 12   Solve the fractional equation $\dfrac{2x+1}{3x+4} = \dfrac{x}{3x-2}$.

Solution

$$\frac{2x+1}{3x+4} = \frac{x}{3x-2}$$

Multiplying both sides by their common denominator, we have

$$\frac{2x+1}{3x+4} \times (3x+4)(3x-2) = \frac{x}{3x-2} \times (3x+4)(3x-2)$$

$$(2x+1)(3x-2) = x(3x+4)$$

$$6x^2 - x - 2 = 3x^2 + 4x$$

$$3x^2 - 5x - 2 = 0$$

$$(3x+1)(x-2) = 0$$

$$\therefore \qquad x = -\frac{1}{3} \quad \text{or} \quad x = 2$$

Note: We must check whether the derived roots cause the 'division-by-zero' error in the fractions in the original equation. If it happens, the root that causes the error must be rejected.

In the above example, verify that $x = -\dfrac{1}{3}$ and $x = 2$ do not cause the 'division-by-zero' error when put into the original equation.

▶ *Try It 12!*   Solve the equation $\dfrac{3x-1}{2x+5} = \dfrac{x-3}{x+4}$.

Example 13 Solve the equation $\dfrac{2}{x-2} + \dfrac{x-3}{x-4} = 2$.

Solution

$$\frac{2}{x-2} + \frac{x-3}{x-4} = 2$$

Multiplying both sides by $(x-2)(x-4)$, we have
$$2(x-4) + (x-3)(x-2) = 2(x-2)(x-4)$$
$$2x - 8 + x^2 - 5x + 6 = 2x^2 - 12x + 16$$
$$x^2 - 9x + 18 = 0$$
$$\therefore \quad (x-3)(x-6) = 0$$
$$x = 3 \quad \text{or} \quad x = 6$$

▶ *Try It 13!* Solve the equation $\dfrac{x+2}{x} + \dfrac{1}{x-2} = 2$.

Exercise 2.5

Basic Practice

1. Solve the following equations.

   (a) $x + \dfrac{1}{x} = 2$

   (b) $\dfrac{x-1}{4} = \dfrac{x}{x+3}$

   (c) $\dfrac{x-1}{2x-5} = \dfrac{x-6}{x+2}$

   (d) $\dfrac{x}{2} + 1 = \dfrac{24}{x}$

   (e) $\dfrac{x-2}{5} = 1 - \dfrac{1}{2x-3}$

   (f) $\dfrac{1}{x+3} + \dfrac{1}{x-3} = \dfrac{5}{8}$

   (g) $\dfrac{(x-2)(x-3)}{(x-1)(x-5)} = \dfrac{5}{3}$

   (h) $\dfrac{7-x}{x+2} - \dfrac{1}{x-1} = \dfrac{1}{3}$

Further Practice

2. Solve the following equations.

   (a) $\dfrac{x}{x-2} + \dfrac{x+7}{x+2} = 5$

   (b) $\dfrac{3}{x-1} - \dfrac{2x+10}{x^2+2x-3} = \dfrac{1}{3}$

   (c) $\dfrac{x-3}{x-5} = 2 - \dfrac{x-5}{x-7}$

   (d) $\dfrac{1}{x+3} - \dfrac{4}{x-3} = 5$

   (e) $\dfrac{1}{x} + \dfrac{2}{x-1} + \dfrac{3}{x+1} = 0$

   (f) $\dfrac{5}{x-15} - \dfrac{2}{x+6} = \dfrac{3}{x-9}$

3. The sum of a number and its reciprocal is $\frac{25}{12}$. Find the number.

4. A tin of 144 sweets is divided equally among x children. Had there been 4 children fewer, each child would have had 6 sweets more. Find the value of x.

Brainworks

5. Consider the following solution of a fractional equation.

$$\frac{5}{x-2} - \frac{4}{x} = \frac{10}{x(x-2)} \quad\text{...(1)}$$

Multiplying both sides by $x(x-2)$, we have

$$x(x-2) \times \left(\frac{5}{x-2} - \frac{4}{x} \right) = x(x-2) \times \frac{10}{x(x-2)} \quad\text{...................(2)}$$
$$5x - 4(x-2) = 10 \quad\text{.............................(3)}$$
$$5x - 4x + 8 = 10 \quad\text{.............................(4)}$$
$$\therefore \qquad\qquad x = 2 \quad\text{.............................(5)}$$

(a) Is the solution $x = 2$ valid?

(b) Among equations (1) to (5), which equations are invalid when $x = 2$?

2.6 Problems Involving Quadratic Equations

Quadratic equations are often involved in solving mathematical, engineering and applied science problems. Let us study some examples.

Example 14   A rectangular cardboard measures 28 cm by 20 cm. A picture of area 300 cm^2 is pasted on the cardboard so as to leave a border of uniform width on all four sides. Find the width of the border.

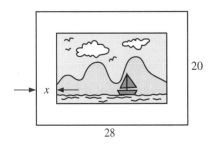

Solution   Let x cm be the width of the border.

Then,   length of the picture $= (28 - 2x)$ cm,
              breadth of the picture $= (20 - 2x)$ cm.

As   area of the picture $= 300$ cm^2,
we have $(28 - 2x)(20 - 2x) = 300$
                $560 - 96x + 4x^2 = 300$
                $4x^2 - 96x + 260 = 0$
                $x^2 - 24x + 65 = 0$

$$x = \frac{-(-24) \pm \sqrt{(-24)^2 - 4(1)(65)}}{2(1)}$$

$$= \frac{24 \pm \sqrt{316}}{2}$$

$= 3.11$ or 20.9 (rejected)

$\therefore$ $x = 3.11$ (correct to 3 sig. fig.)

i.e. the width of the border is 3.11 cm.

Can you remember the steps in solving word problems? Try to identify each step on your own.

Recall

Note: The width of the border should be less than half of the breadth of the cardboard, i.e. 10 cm. Therefore, the root $x = 20.9$ is rejected.

▶ *Try It 14!*   A rectangular swimming pool measures 20 m by 16 m. A path of uniform width is built around the pool. If the area of the path is 100 m^2, find the width of the path, giving your answer correct to 3 significant figures.

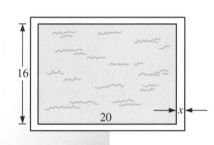

Example 15   A certain number of people promised to invest equally in a new business project costing \$24 000. Three of them failed to provide the money; therefore each of the remaining investors had to pay \$400 more to make up the sum. How many people had promised to invest initially?

Solution   Let n be the number of people who promised to invest initially.

Amount that should have been invested per person $= \$\dfrac{24\ 000}{n}$

When 3 people quit,

the number of the remaining people who invested $= n - 3$,

actual amount invested per person $= \$\dfrac{24\ 000}{n - 3}$.

An important use of quadratic equations is in mechanics, the study of the motion of objects and their interactions with forces. When an object moves in a trajectory, its path of motion is parabolic in shape and such paths can be described using quadratic equations. The curves of these quadratic equations take on the basic shape of the curve of $y = -x^2$.

MathsBits

As extra amount invested per person = $400,

$$\frac{24\,000}{n-3} - \frac{24\,000}{n} = 400$$

$$n(n-3)\left(\frac{24\,000}{n-3} - \frac{24\,000}{n}\right) = 400n(n-3)$$

$$24\,000n - 24\,000(n-3) = 400n^2 - 1200n$$

$$24\,000n - 24\,000n + 72\,000 = 400n^2 - 1200n$$

$$400n^2 - 1200n - 72\,000 = 0$$

$$n^2 - 3n - 180 = 0$$

$$(n-15)(n+12) = 0$$

$$n = 15 \quad \text{or} \quad -12 \quad \text{(rejected)}$$

∴ 15 people promised to invest initially.

Try It 15! Mrs Li spent $300 to buy a certain type of tea. If the price of the tea had been reduced by $50 per kg, she could have bought 0.5 kg more. Find the original price per kg of the tea.

Example 16 The distance between two towns, A and B, is 120 km. Mr Singh drove from A to B at an average speed of v km/h. On his return journey, his average speed was 5 km/h greater than his average speed from A to B, and hence the time taken was 20 minutes less. Find the value of v.

Solution His average speed for the return journey = $(v + 5)$ km/h.

Time taken from A to B = $\dfrac{120}{v}$ hours

Time taken from B to A = $\dfrac{120}{v+5}$ hours

As the return time taken was 20 minutes less,

$$\frac{120}{v} - \frac{120}{v+5} = \frac{20}{60}$$

Multiplying both sides by $v(v + 5)$, we have

$$120(v+5) - 120v = \frac{1}{3}v(v+5)$$

$$600 \times 3 = v^2 + 5v$$

$$v^2 + 5v - 1800 = 0$$

$$(v-40)(v+45) = 0$$

$$v = 40 \quad \text{or} \quad -45 \quad \text{(rejected)}$$

$$\therefore \qquad v = 40$$

> *As the time taken is expressed in hours, the 20 minutes must be expressed in hours in the equation.*

Remark

Try It 16! A cyclist cycles at a constant speed from P to Q, a distance 60 km apart. If he had increased his speed by 3 km/h, the time taken would have been 40 minutes less. Find his speed.

Exercise 2.6

Basic Practice

1. The product of two consecutive positive integers is 1260. Find the integers.

2. The sum of the squares of two consecutive positive odd numbers is 650. Find the numbers.

3. The height of a triangle is 3 cm less than its base. The area of the triangle is 90 cm^2. Find the base of the triangle.

4. The perimeter of a rectangle is 68 cm and its area is 253 cm^2. Suppose the length of the rectangle is x cm.
   (a) Express the breadth of the rectangle in terms of x.
   (b) Find the dimensions of the rectangle.

5. When the length of each side of a square is increased by 5 cm, its area is increased by 145 cm^2. Let x cm be the original length of the square.
   (a) Express the new length of the square in terms of x.
   (b) Express the new area of the square in terms of x.
   (c) Find the value of x.

6. A rectangle is 24 cm long and 17 cm wide. When its length decreases by x cm and its breadth increases by x cm, its area is increased by 12 cm^2.
   (a) Express, in terms of x,
      (i) the new length,
      (ii) the new breadth,
      (iii) the new area of the rectangle.
   (b) Find the value of x.

7. The sum of the ages of Mingfa and his father is 34 years. In 4 years' time, the square of Mingfa's age will be equal to his father's age. Find Mingfa's present age.

8. A piece of wire is 76 cm long. It is cut into two unequal parts and each part is bent into a square. The sum of the areas of the two squares is 205 cm^2. Find the length of the shorter part of the wire.

Further Practice

9. The sum of the squares of three consecutive positive even numbers is 2360. Find the smallest number.

10. On a 21 cm by 29 cm rectangular sheet of paper, the typing area is a rectangle of area 380 cm². There are margins of equal width on all four sides of the paper. Find the width of a margin, giving your answer correct to the nearest 0.1 cm.

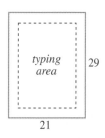

11. At noon, Ada left junction T and walked due north. At 1.00 p.m., Bob left junction T and walked due east. Both of them walked at a speed of 4 km/h. At what time would they be 10 km apart? Give your answer correct to the nearest minute.

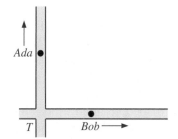

12. A rod AB, 65 cm long, leans against a vertical wall. Its lower end B is 25 cm from the wall. When it slides down to the position DE, it is found that $AD = BE$.
   (a) Find the length of AC.
   (b) Find the length of AD.

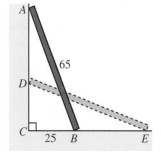

13. A shop owner spent $540 on computer keyboards. If the price of each keyboard had been reduced by $2, he could have bought 3 more keyboards. Find the price of one keyboard.

14. The distance between two stations, A and B, is 100 km. If the average speed of a train is increased by 5 km/h, the time taken by the train to travel from A to B would be 10 minutes less. Find the original average speed of the train, giving your answer correct to 3 significant figures.

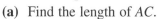

Maths@Work

15. The distance s metres travelled by a car in time t seconds after the first observation is given by

$$s = 3t^2 + 4t.$$

Find the time taken for the car to travel 100 m, giving your answer correct to 3 significant figures.

16.

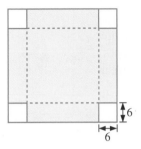

6

6

The figure shows a square cardboard. A 6-cm square is cut from each of its corners and the figure is then folded along the dotted lines to form a square tray. If the volume of the tray is 2000 cm³, find the length of a side of the cardboard, correct to 3 significant figures.

17. A group of people hired a boat for $1200 and each person paid an equal amount for it. Five people did not turn up, so each person on the trip had to pay $8 more. Find the number of people in the group who went on the trip.

18. The numerator of a positive fraction is 2 less than its denominator. When both the numerator and the denominator are increased by 3, the new fraction is greater than the original one by $\dfrac{1}{18}$. Find the original fraction.

Brainworks

19. A shop owner has 80 copies of a computer game. Based on past experience, if the price is set at $60 per copy, all of them will be sold. For each $5 increase in price, an additional 4 copies of the game will be unsold.
   (a) If the price is set at $70 per copy,
      (i) find the number of copies that will be sold,
      (ii) find the total sales amount.
   (b) If the total sales amount is $5100, find the price per copy of the game.
   (c) What should the price per copy be in order to get the maximum total sales amount?
[Assume that the price per copy of the game is a multiple of 5 in **(b)** and **(c)**.]

In A Nutshell

1. Four Methods of Solving a Quadratic Equation

(a) Factorisation method

$$ax^2 + bx + c = 0$$

By factorisation,

$$(px + q)(rx + s) = 0$$

$$x = -\frac{q}{p} \quad \text{or} \quad x = -\frac{s}{r}$$

(b) Graphical method

By drawing the graph of

$$y = ax^2 + bx + c.$$

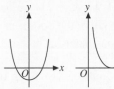

| real and unequal roots | real and equal roots | No real roots |

(c) Completing the square method

$$x^2 + bx + c = 0$$

By completing the square,

$$\left(x + \frac{b}{2}\right)^2 = q$$

$$x + \frac{b}{2} = \pm\sqrt{q}$$

$$\therefore \quad x = -\frac{b}{2} \pm \sqrt{q}$$

When $q < 0$, there are no real roots.

(d) Quadratic formula

The roots of $ax^2 + bx + c = 0$ are:

$$x = \frac{-b \pm \sqrt{b^2 - 4ac}}{2a}$$

When $b^2 - 4ac < 0$, there are no real roots.

2. Fractional Equations

$$\frac{a}{x - p} + \frac{b}{x - q} = c$$

$$(x - p)(x - q)\left(\frac{a}{x - p} + \frac{b}{x - q}\right) = c(x - p)(x - q)$$

$$a(x - q) + b(x - p) = c(x - p)(x - q)$$

- The fractional equation is first converted into a quadratic equation.

- Ensure that the roots of the quadratic equation do not give rise to 'division-by-zero' error in the original equation. If this happens, we need to reject $x = p$ or $x = q$.

Revision Exercise 2

1. Solve the following equations by factorisation.
   (a) $2x^2 + x - 15 = 0$
   (b) $3x^2 - 20x - 7 = 0$
   (c) $9x^2 - 25 = 0$
   (d) $(x + 3)(x - 2) = 5x(x - 2)$

2. Solve the following equations by the method of completing the square.
   (a) $x^2 - 6x + 4 = 0$
   (b) $x^2 + 4x - 3 = 0$
   (c) $x^2 + 5x + 8 = 0$
   (d) $x^2 - 7x - 2 = 0$

3. **(a)** Draw the graph of $y = x^2 + 3x - 6$ for $-5 \leqslant x \leqslant 2$.
   (b) Use your graph to solve the equation $x^2 + 3x - 6 = 0$. Give your answers correct to 1 decimal place.

4. Solve the following equations by using the quadratic formula, giving your answers correct to 3 significant figures where necessary.
   (a) $x^2 + 3x - 88 = 0$
   (b) $36x^2 + 12x + 1 = 0$
   (c) $4x^2 - 5x + 9 = 0$
   (d) $5x^2 - 8x - 2 = 0$

5. Solve the following fractional equations.
   (a) $\dfrac{x + 1}{2} = \dfrac{8}{x + 1}$
   (b) $10(x - 2) + \dfrac{10}{x - 2} = 29$
   (c) $\dfrac{x}{x + 1} + \dfrac{x + 1}{x} = 3$
   (d) $\dfrac{3}{7x - 2} - \dfrac{2}{7x + 3} = \dfrac{3}{4}$

6. Solve the following equations by using any method.
   (a) $3x^2 + 7x + 1 = 0$
   (b) $(2x - 1)^2 = (x + 1)^2$
   (c) $(x + 3)(2x - 9) = x(x + 2)$
   (d) $\dfrac{1}{3x} + \dfrac{2}{3x - 1} + \dfrac{3}{3x + 1} = 0$

7. A rectangular flower bed measures 30 m by 20 m. It is surrounded by a path of uniform width. The area of the path is $\dfrac{1}{3}$ of the area of the flower bed. Find the width of the path correct to 3 significant figures.

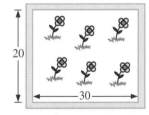

8. The distance travelled by a train is 180 km. If the average speed of the train is increased by 10 km/h, the time taken by the train would be 15 minutes less. Find the train's average speed.

9. The diagram shows a ring that is bounded by two circles of radii R cm and r cm. The difference in the circumference of the two circles is 12 cm.

    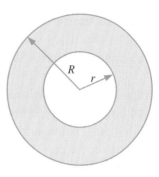

    (a) Express R in terms of r and π.

    (b) If the area of the ring is 50 cm², find the value of r correct to 3 significant figures.

10. The distance between two towns, A and B, is 100 km. Mr Jones drove from A to B at an average speed of v km/h.

    (a) Write down an expression, in terms of v, for the time, in hours, that he took to complete the journey from A to B. [1]

    (b) On the return journey, his average speed was 6 km/h greater than his speed from A to B. Write down an expression, in terms of v, for

        (i) his speed for the journey from B to A. [1]

        (ii) the time, in hours that he took for the journey from B to A. [1]

    (c) Given also that the return journey took 20 minutes less than the journey from A to B, form an equation in v, and show that it reduces to
    $$v^2 + 6v - 1800 = 0.$$
    [3]

    (d) Solve the equation $v^2 + 6v - 1800 = 0$, giving both answers correct to three significant figures. [4]

    (e) Calculate, correct to the nearest minute, the **total** time that Mr Jones spent travelling. [2]

    NP2/2000/11

11. (a) Express as a single fraction in its simplest form
    $$\frac{200}{x} - \frac{200}{x+4}.$$
    [2]

    (b) When driven in town, a car runs x kilometres on each litre of petrol.

        (i) Find, in terms of x, the number of litres of petrol used when the car is driven 200 km in town. [1]

        (ii) When driven out of town, the car runs $(x + 4)$ kilometres on each litre of petrol. It uses 5 litres less petrol to go 200 km out of town than to go 200 km in town.

        Use this information to write down an equation involving x, and show that it simplifies to
    $$x^2 + 4x - 160 = 0.$$
    [3]

    (c) Solve the equation $x^2 + 4x - 160 = 0$, giving both answers correct to two decimal places. [4]

    (d) Calculate the **total** volume of petrol used when the car is driven 40 km in town and then 120 km out of town. [2]

    NP2/2001/7

12. A polar explorer is planning an expedition. He investigates three possible routes.

(a) If he travels on route A, which is 800 km long, he expects to cover x km per day.

Route B, which is the same distance as route A, has more difficult ice conditions and he would only expect to cover $(x - 5)$ km per day.

Route C, which is 100 km longer than route A, has easier conditions and he would expect to cover $(x + 5)$ km per day.

Write down an expression, in terms of x, for the number of days that he expects to take on

(i) route A,

(ii) route B,

(iii) route C. [2]

(b) He estimates that route C will take 20 days less than route B.

Form an equation in x, and show that it reduces to

$$x^2 + 5x - 450 = 0.$$ [4]

(c) Solve the equation $x^2 + 5x - 450 = 0$, giving both answers correct to 1 decimal place. [4]

(d) Calculate the number of days that he expects to take on route A. [2]

NP2/2003/8

Extend Your Learning Curve

Sum and Product of Roots

Suppose α and β are the roots of a quadratic equation $ax^2 + bx + c = 0$.

The sum of the roots, $\alpha + \beta$, and the product of the roots, $\alpha\beta$, can be expressed in terms of the coefficients a and b, and the constant c. Find the expressions for $\alpha + \beta$ and $\alpha\beta$ in terms of a, b and/or c.

Write In Your Journal

You have learnt four methods of solving quadratic equations. Which method do you find easiest to use and which do you find most challenging? Write about the ease or difficulty that you encountered in using both methods.

3 Linear Inequalities

A company decides to organise a new product launch at a hotel. The hotel charges a rental fee of $500 for a function room and $30 for beverage and food for each guest. If the company's budget is $3000 for this event, what is the maximum possible number of guests that the company can invite for the launch? We may apply inequalities to solve this type of problem.

Let's learn to...

- understand the basic properties of inequalities
- solve linear inequalities in one unknown
- solve simultaneous linear inequalities in one unknown
- represent the solution of a linear inequality on the number line
- apply linear inequalities to solve everyday problems

3.1 Basic Properties Of Inequalities

In Secondary 1, we have learnt that real numbers can be represented on a number line and then compared based on their relative positions.

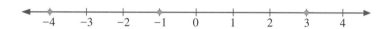

For example,

> −4 is on the left of −1, ∴ −4 is less than −1 and is denoted by $−4 < −1$;
> 3 is on the right of −1, ∴ 3 is greater than −1 and is denoted by $3 > −1$.

Therefore, for the comparison of two numbers, we have the following relationship:

> For any two numbers, a and b, one and only one of the following relationships hold:
>
> $$a < b \quad \text{or} \quad a = b \quad \text{or} \quad a > b$$

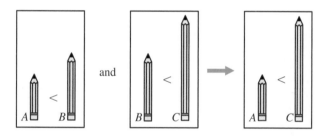

If pencil A is shorter than pencil B and pencil B is shorter than pencil C, it is therefore obvious that pencil A is shorter than pencil C. Thus, we have the following property:

> If $a < b$ and $b < c$, then $a < c$.

Example 1 It is given that $a < 5$. Is $a < 9$?

Solution $a < 5$
and $5 < 9$.

Thus,

$a < 9$.

▶ *Try It 1!*   It is given that $p < 0$. Is $p < 2$?

Let us explore other properties of inequalities.

Class Activity 1

If each box represents an inequality sign '<' or '>', what should it be in each case?

1. (a) 3 ▢ 5, 3 + 6 ▢ 5 + 6

(b) –9 ▢ 2, –9 + 3 ▢ 2 + 3

(c) 7 ▢ 10, 7 – 8 ▢ 10 – 8

(d) If $a < b$, then $a + c$ ▢ $b + c$.

2. (a) 2 ▢ 8, 2 × 5 ▢ 8 × 5

(b) –3 ▢ –1, –3 × 7 ▢ –1 × 7

(c) –12 ▢ 6, $-12 \times \frac{1}{2}$ ▢ $6 \times \frac{1}{2}$

(d) If $a < b$, and $c > 0$, then ac ▢ bc.

3. (a) 4 ▢ 7, 4 × (–3) ▢ 7 × (–3)

(b) –15 ▢ 10, $-15 \times \left(-\frac{2}{5}\right)$ ▢ $10 \times \left(-\frac{2}{5}\right)$

(c) –28 ▢ –14, $-28 \times \left(-\frac{3}{7}\right)$ ▢ $-14 \times \left(-\frac{3}{7}\right)$

(d) If $a < b$ and $c < 0$, then ac ▢ bc.

From Class Activity 1, we see that when a number is added to or subtracted from both sides of an inequality, the inequality holds.

$$\text{If } a < b, \text{ then } a + c < b + c.$$

Since subtracting c is the same as adding $-c$, we do not write the law for subtraction separately.

When both sides of an inequality are multiplied by a non-zero number c, the inequality holds for $c > 0$, but the inequality sign is reversed for $c < 0$.

$$\text{If } a < b \text{ and } c > 0, \text{ then } ac < bc.$$
$$\text{If } a < b \text{ and } c < 0, \text{ then } ac > bc.$$

There are similar properties for the cases, $a \leq b$, $a > b$ and $a \geq b$. Try to write them down yourself.

Example 2 It is given that $a < b$. Compare the values of the following pairs of numbers.

(a) $a + 3$ and $b + 3$ (b) $\frac{1}{2}a$ and $\frac{1}{2}b$

(c) $-a$ and $-b$

Solution (a) Since $\qquad a < b,$

$\therefore \qquad a + 3 < b + 3.$

(b) Since $\qquad a < b$ and $\frac{1}{2} > 0,$

$\therefore \qquad \frac{1}{2}a < \frac{1}{2}b.$

(c) Since $\qquad a < b$ and $-1 < 0,$

$\therefore \qquad (-1)a > (-1)b$ The inequality sign is reversed.

i.e. $\qquad -a > -b.$

▶ *Try It 2!* It is given that $p < q$. Compare the values of the following pairs of numbers.

(a) $p - 1$ and $q - 1$ (b) $-4p$ and $-4q$

(c) $\frac{1}{5}p$ and $\frac{1}{5}q$

Exercise 3.1

(**Basic Practice**)

1. If $a < 7$, determine whether the following inequalities are true.
   (a) $a < 10$ (b) $a < 2$
   (c) $a + 2 < 9$ (d) $-a < -7$

2. If $p > -5$, determine whether the following inequalities are true.
   (a) $p > -3$ (b) $p > -9$
   (c) $p + 5 > 0$ (d) $-p < -5$

3. Copy and fill in each box with an inequality sign.

   (a) If $a < b$, then $a - 6 \ \boxed{} \ b - 6.$

   (b) If $p > q$, then $p + 7 \ \boxed{} \ q + 7.$

   (c) If $r \leq s$, then $2r \ \boxed{} \ 2s.$

   (d) If $x \geq y$, then $-\frac{x}{3} \ \boxed{} \ -\frac{y}{3}.$

4. Copy and fill in each box with an inequality sign.
   (a) If $a < b$, then

   (i) $4a$ ▢ $4b$,

   (ii) $4a + 3$ ▢ $4b + 3$.

   (b) If $m \geqslant n$, then

   (i) $-m$ ▢ $-n$,

   (ii) $1 - m$ ▢ $1 - n$.

5. If $p \leqslant q$, compare the values of the following pairs of numbers.
   (a) $2p - 7$ and $2q - 7$
   (b) $-4 - \dfrac{1}{5}p$ and $-4 - \dfrac{1}{5}q$

Maths@Work

6. (a) If $a < b$ and $c < d$, what is the inequality relationship between
      (i) $a + c$ and $b + c$,
      (ii) $b + c$ and $b + d$,
      (iii) $a + c$ and $b + d$?
   (b) If Mr and Mrs Tan's monthly salaries are more than $4000 and $3500 respectively, what can you say about their total monthly salary?

Brainworks

7. If $a < b$ and $c < d$, is it necessary that $a - c < b - d$? If it is not true, give a counter-example.

8. If $a < b$, must a^2 be less than b^2?

3.2 Linear Inequalities In One Unknown

Using the properties of inequalities learnt in the previous section, we can solve inequalities in one unknown like

$$3x + 5 < 17 \quad \text{and} \quad 4x - 9 \geqslant 7x + 8.$$

Inequalities of these forms are called **linear inequalities in one unknown**.

Example 3 Solve the inequality $3x + 5 < 17$.

Solution
$$3x + 5 < 17$$
$$3x + 5 - 5 < 17 - 5 \qquad \text{Subtract 5 from both sides.}$$
$$3x < 12$$
$$\frac{3x}{3} < \frac{12}{3} \qquad \text{Divide both sides by 3.}$$
$$\therefore \qquad x < 4$$

 **Try It 3!** Solve the inequality $2x + 3 < 15$.

The solution of an inequality can also be represented by an interval on a number line. For example, the number line below shows the solution $x < 4$.

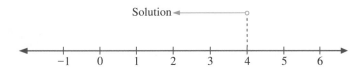

The small **hollow circle** indicates that the solution **excludes** the value $x = 4$.

Example 4 Solve the inequality $2x - 19 \leqslant 7x + 6$. Represent the solution on a number line.

Solution
$$2x - 19 \leqslant 7x + 6$$
$$2x - 19 + 19 \leqslant 7x + 6 + 19 \qquad \text{Add 19 to both sides.}$$
$$2x \leqslant 7x + 25$$
$$2x - 7x \leqslant 7x + 25 - 7x \qquad \text{Subtract } 7x \text{ from both sides.}$$
$$-5x \leqslant 25$$
$$\frac{-5x}{-5} \geqslant \frac{25}{-5} \qquad \begin{array}{l}\text{Divide both sides by } -5.\\ \text{(Note the reversal of the inequality sign.)}\end{array}$$
$$\therefore \qquad x \geqslant -5$$

Explore some advanced examples of linear inequalities at http:// www.analyzemath.com/ Linear_Inequalities/ Linear_Inequalities_Tutor.html

The number line above shows the solution $x \geqslant 5$. The **solid circle** indicates that the solution **includes** the value $x = -5$.

 Try It 4! Solve the inequality $3x - 8 \leqslant 7x + 16$. Represent the solution on a number line.

Example 5 Solve the inequality $\dfrac{2x+3}{4} \geqslant \dfrac{5x-1}{6}$. Represent the solution on a number line.

Solution

$$\dfrac{2x+3}{4} \geqslant \dfrac{5x-1}{6}$$

$$12 \times \dfrac{2x+3}{4} \geqslant 12 \times \dfrac{5x-1}{6}$$ Multiply both sides by 12, as 12 is the LCM of the denominators 4 and 6.

$$3(2x+3) \geqslant 2(5x-1)$$

$$6x+9 \geqslant 10x-2$$

$$6x \geqslant 10x-11$$ Subtract 9 from both sides.

$$-4x \geqslant -11$$ Subtract 10x from both sides.

$$x \leqslant \dfrac{-11}{-4}$$ Divide both sides by −4.

$$\therefore \quad x \leqslant \dfrac{11}{4}$$

In general, if $a \neq 0$, the solution of $ax + b < c$ is

$$x < \dfrac{c-b}{a} \ (if \ a > 0)$$

or $\ x > \dfrac{c-b}{a} \ (if \ a < 0).$

Remark

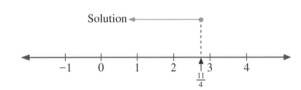

Solution ←————————●

$$\overleftarrow{ \underset{-1}{|} \quad \underset{0}{|} \quad \underset{1}{|} \quad \underset{2}{|} \quad \underset{\substack{\uparrow \\ \frac{11}{4}}}{|} \underset{3}{|} \quad \underset{4}{|} } \rightarrow$$

The number line above shows the solution $x \leqslant \dfrac{11}{4}$.

▶ **Try It 5!** Solve the inequality $\dfrac{x-4}{5} \geqslant \dfrac{2x+1}{7}$. Represent the solution on a number line.

Exercise 3.2

Basic Practice

1. Solve the following inequalities and represent each solution on a number line.

    (a) $x - 2 < 7$

    (b) $x + 3 \geqslant 4$

    (c) $\dfrac{x}{5} \leqslant 2$

    (d) $4x > 12$

    (e) $3x + 5 \geqslant 2$

    (f) $7x - 13 < 1$

    (g) $9x - 2 < 4x + 8$

    (h) $6x + 7 \geqslant 8x - 5$

Further Practice

2. Solve the following inequalities and represent each solution on a number line.

(a) $5(2x + 3) > 4(x - 2) - 13$ (b) $11 - 2(3x - 7) \leqslant 6(9 - 2x)$

(c) $\dfrac{x}{3} + 1 > \dfrac{5}{6}$ (d) $\dfrac{2x - 1}{5} < \dfrac{x}{2}$

(e) $\dfrac{2}{7} + \dfrac{x}{4} \leqslant \dfrac{3x}{4} - \dfrac{5}{7}$ (f) $\dfrac{2(3x + 1)}{5} \geqslant \dfrac{3(x - 1)}{8}$

(g) $\dfrac{4x - 5}{3} - \dfrac{1}{4} > \dfrac{1 - x}{9}$ (h) $\dfrac{x - 3}{2} > \dfrac{4}{13}(2x + 5) - 1$

(i) $\dfrac{x + 1}{2} - \dfrac{x - 1}{3} \leqslant \dfrac{2x - 7}{4}$ (j) $\dfrac{2x - 1}{5} + \dfrac{x + 1}{3} < 2 - \dfrac{3x - 2}{4}$

Maths@Work

3. The maximum loading of electric current on a power board is 13 Amperes (A). A lamp of $\dfrac{1}{2}$A is already plugged into it. How many hairdryers of 3A can be plugged into the power board and turned on without overloading it?

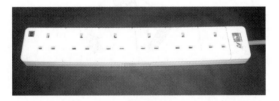

power board

Brainworks

4. Write a linear inequality in the form $ax + b < cx + d$ such that the solution is $x > 8$, where a, b, c and d are constants.

3.3   Simultaneous Linear Inequalities

Sometimes, an unknown x has to satisfy two or more linear inequalities simultaneously. We use the word "and" to connect those inequalities. Then the solution of x is the **common solution** to all those simultaneous linear inequalities.

Example 6   Solve the inequalities $2x + 3 < 9$ and $3x - 7 < 8$.

Solution   First, we find the solution to each inequality.

$$2x + 3 < 9 \quad \text{and} \quad 3x - 7 < 8$$
$$2x < 6 \qquad\qquad 3x < 15$$
$$x < 3 \qquad\qquad\quad x < 5$$

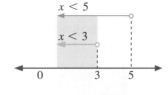

Since x satisfies $x < 3$ and $x < 5$, we find the common part of both solutions.

∴ the required solution is $x < 3$.

▶ *Try It 6!*   Solve the inequalities $5x - 8 < 12$ and $7x + 3 < 17$.

A sketch of the individual solutions on a number line may help you visualise the solution for the simultaneous linear inequalities.

Example 7   Solve the inequalities $5x + 13 \geqslant 2x - 5$ and $3x - 7 > 9x + 11$.

Solution

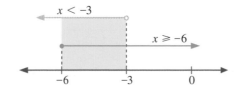

$$5x + 13 \geqslant 2x - 5 \quad \text{and} \quad 3x - 7 > 9x + 11$$
$$5x \geqslant 2x - 18 \qquad\qquad 3x > 9x + 18$$
$$3x \geqslant -18 \qquad\qquad\quad -6x > 18$$
$$x \geqslant -6 \qquad\qquad\qquad x < -3$$

∴ the required solution is $-6 \leqslant x < -3$.

▶ *Try It 7!*   Solve the inequalities $6x + 9 \leqslant 2x + 13$ and $2x - 8 < 7x + 12$.

Example 8 Solve the inequalities $\frac{x+1}{3} < \frac{x-2}{4} < x$.

Solution The given inequalities are equivalent to 2 simultaneous linear inequalities.

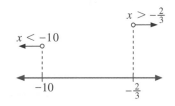

$$\frac{x+1}{3} < \frac{x-2}{4} \quad \text{and} \quad \frac{x-2}{4} < x$$
$$4(x+1) < 3(x-2) \quad \text{and} \quad x-2 < 4x$$
$$4x+4 < 3x-6 \quad \text{and} \quad x < 4x+2$$
$$4x < 3x-10 \quad \text{and} \quad -3x < 2$$
$$x < -10 \quad \text{and} \quad x > -\frac{2}{3}$$

There is no real number x which is less than -10 and greater than $-\frac{2}{3}$.

∴ the given inequalities have no solution.

▶ *Try It 8!* Solve the inequalities $\frac{x+1}{2} < x < \frac{2x-5}{3}$.

Exercise 3.3

Basic Practice

1. Solve each of the following pairs of simultaneous inequalities. Represent the solution on a number line.

   (a) $x+1 > 3$ and $3x > 15$

   (b) $x-1 \leqslant -4$ and $3x-5 \leqslant 4$

   (c) $2x+5 \leqslant 0$ and $7x-1 \geqslant 13$

   (d) $5x-3 < 2$ and $4x+7 \geqslant x+3$

   (e) $6x+2 \geqslant 3x+11$ and $9x-4 > 5x$

   (f) $9-2x < 7-x$ and $11-6x < 8-10x$

   (g) $\frac{x}{2} - 1 > 3$ and $\frac{2x}{5} - 3 \leqslant x$

   (h) $\frac{x-1}{4} \geqslant \frac{x+1}{3}$ and $\frac{5-2x}{7} > 1$

Further Practice

2. Solve the following simultaneous inequalities.

   (a) $2(4x+1) > 3(5x-2)$ and $3(2x-6) < 5(x+1)$

   (b) $\frac{3}{4}(x-2) > x+5$ and $9-x < \frac{2}{7}(3x+1)$

   (c) $-5 < 2x+1 \leqslant 11$

   (d) $3x-5 < 31 < 2x-7$

   (e) $3(x-2) < 5(x+1) < 3-x$

   (f) $\frac{x}{3} \leqslant \frac{x-2}{2} \leqslant \frac{3x+7}{4}$

3. Find the integer values of x which satisfy the inequalities $-2 < \dfrac{5x-1}{8} \leqslant 3$.

4. Find the smallest integer value of x which satisfies the inequalities $2x - 3 \leqslant 4x + 6$ and $8x - 1 > 5x - 7$.

Maths@Work

5. A surveyor found that a rectangular playground is 20 m long and 13 m wide, corrected to the nearest metre. Suppose the actual length of the playground is x m and the breadth is y m.
   (a) Write down an inequality for the range of the values of
      (i) x,   (ii) y.
   (b) Find the range of the values of
      (i)   the perimeter of the playground,
      (ii) the area of the playground.

Brainworks

6. Find a possible set of integer values for a, b and c such that the solution to the inequalities $ax + 3 > 2x + b$ and $cx - 1 > 5x - 4$ is
   (a) $x < -2$,   (b) $-3 < x < 4$.

3.4 Applications Of Linear Inequalities

Linear inequalities can help us to solve some everyday problems. Let us study some examples.

Example 9   A potted plant is 11 cm tall and grows 3 cm a week. After how many complete weeks will it first be taller than 40 cm?

Solution   Let x be the number of weeks after the current date.
The height of the plant after xth week $= (11 + 3x)$ cm.

$$11 + 3x > 40$$
$$3x > 29$$
$$x > \frac{29}{3}$$
$$x > 9\frac{2}{3}$$

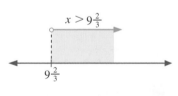

∴ the smallest integer value of x is 10.
∴ the plant will first be taller than 40 cm after 10 weeks.

▶ *Try It 9!*   Saadiah has $70 in her money box. She saves $40 every month in her money box. What is the minimum number of complete months required in order for Saadiah to have more than $500 in her money box?

Example 10 To receive a grade B for a course, a candidate must have a mean score of at least 80 but less than 90 in three examination papers. The full score in each paper is 100. Jinlan scored 83 and 75 in the first two papers. What score should she have in the third paper in order to get a grade B for the course?

Solution   Let x be Jinlan's score in the third paper.

$$\text{Mean score for the 3 papers} = \frac{83 + 75 + x}{3}$$

∴ we require

$$80 \leqslant \frac{83 + 75 + x}{3} < 90$$

$$80 \leqslant \frac{158 + x}{3} < 90$$

$240 \leqslant$	$158 + x$	< 270	Multiply by 3.
$82 \leqslant$	x	< 112	Subtract 158.

But the full score in the third paper is 100,
∴ Jinlan's required score is in the range $82 \leqslant x \leqslant 100$.

Note: **1.** In this example of simultaneous linear inequalities, the unknown x only appears in the middle expression. Thus we can solve the inequalities without having to split them into two separate inequalities.

2. When solving a word problem involving inequalities, we have to observe the physical restrictions imposed. In this example, the maximum score in a paper is 100.

▶ *Try It 10!*   A student will get a grade C in an ability test if the mean score of three examination papers is more than 60 but less than or equal to 75. Susan scored 57 and 69 in the first two papers. For her to get a grade C, what should her score in the third paper be?
(Assume that the maximum score of each paper is 100.)

Exercise 3.4

(**Basic Practice**)

1. The price of a chocolate bar is $2. Nancy was told by her mother that she should not spend more than $13 on chocolate bars. How many chocolate bars could she buy?

2. A mathematics examination consists of Papers I and II. The full score in each paper is 100. Ali scored 57 in Paper I. If his total score has to be at least 120 in order to pass the examination, what should he score in Paper II?

3. Mr Leong has six $10-notes and some $50-notes in his wallet. If the total value of the notes is less than $400, how many $50-notes are there?

4. In a chemical reaction, the mass of a product grows at a rate of 11 g per hour. The current mass of the product is 46 g. When will the mass of the product first exceed 101 g?

5. The mass of Rohana was 72 kg. After joining a slim-fit programme, her mass decreased at a rate of 3 kg per month. Find the least number of complete months that Rohana has to be on the programme before her mass becomes less than 54 kg.

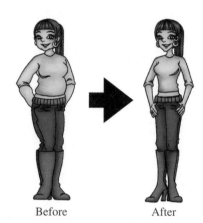

Before   After

Further Practice

6. Water at 24 °C is poured into a boiler. The temperature of the water in the boiler increases by 7 °C per minute. Find the time range at which the temperature of the water in the boiler is greater than 52 °C but less than 73°.

7. A rectangular frame is $(2x + 1)$ cm long and x cm wide. If the perimeter of the frame is not less than 38 cm and not greater than 80 cm, find the range of possible values of x.

x

$2x + 1$

8. The sides of a triangle are $(x - 8)$ cm, $(x - 11)$ cm and $(x + 4)$ cm. Find the range of possible values of x.
(*Hint*: The sum of any two sides of a triangle is greater than the third side.)

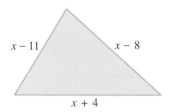

$x - 11$ $x - 8$

$x + 4$

Maths@Work

9. Company A quotes a rental rate for a car at $45 per day. Company B quotes a rate of $38 per day, but with an initial charge of $75. Find the minimum number of complete days of rental required such that the charges by Company B will become cheaper than those by Company A.

10. A community centre plans to have a fundraising concert. There are 100 VIP tickets and 500 general tickets. A VIP ticket costs $50 more than a general ticket. What should be the minimum price of a general ticket so that the funds raised would be at least $20 000?

Brainworks

11. The population of Singapore in 2004 was 4.240 million. Assume that the population of Singapore grows by 0.06 million every year.
   (a) Find the population of Singapore
      (i) in 2005,
      (ii) in 2006,
      (iii) x years after 2004.
   (b) In which year will the population of Singapore first reach 5 million?
   (c) "The population increases by a fixed number of people every year." Is this assumption reasonable? Give your reason(s).

In A Nutshell

Basic Properties of Inequalities

1. If $a < b$, then $a + c < b + c$.
2. If $a < b$ and $c > 0$, then $ac < bc$.
3. If $a < b$ and $c < 0$, then $ac > bc$.

Linear Inequalities in One Unknown

If $a \neq 0$, the solution of $ax + b < c$ is

$$x < \frac{c - b}{a} \quad \text{(if } a > 0)$$

or $\quad x > \dfrac{c - b}{a} \quad \text{(if } a < 0).$

Simultaneous Linear Inequalities

Suppose $a < b$.

Inequalities	Solution	Solution on a number line
1. $x < a$ and $x \leq b$	$x < a$	
2. $x > a$ and $x \geq b$	$x \geq b$	
3. $x < a$ and $x \geq b$	no solution	
4. $x > a$ and $x \leq b$	$a < x \leq b$	

Revision Exercise 3

1. State whether each of the following statements is **true** or **false**. If it is false, give a numerical example to support your claim.
   (a) If $x > 0$, then $x^2 > x$.

   (b) If $x < 0$, then $\frac{1}{x} > 0$.

   (c) If $x > 0$, then $-\frac{1}{x} < 0$.

   (d) If $a < 0$ and $b < 0$, then $a + b < 0$.

   (e) If $a < b$, then $\frac{1}{a} > \frac{1}{b}$.

2. If $a < 7$, state which of the following statements are **true**.
   (a) $a < 17$
   (b) $-a < -7$
   (c) $3a + 4 < 25$
   (d) $a^2 < 49$

3. Solve each of the following linear inequalities and represent the solution on a number line.
   (a) $4x + 9 < -11$
   (b) $15 - 2x \geqslant 23$

   (c) $7(3x - 5) > 6(2x + 1)$
   (d) $\frac{5x - 8}{11} \leqslant 2$

4. Solve the following linear inequalities.

   (a) $\frac{x}{5} - 2(x - 3) < 4$
   (b) $\frac{x}{2} - \frac{x}{3} \geqslant -13$

   (c) $\frac{7 - x}{4} \leqslant \frac{1 - 3x}{6}$
   (d) $(x - 1)^2 < (x + 9)^2$

5. (a) Solve the equation $6x^2 + x - 15 = 0$.
   (b) Solve the linear inequality $19x + 7 < 4(4x + 1)$.
   (c) Which root in (a) satisfies the inequality in (b)?

6. Solve the following simultaneous linear inequalities.

   (a) $3(2x + 1) < 2(9 - 5x)$ and $\frac{2x}{5} - \frac{3x}{7} < 1 - \frac{x}{2}$

   (b) $-8 \leqslant 5x + 2 < 37$
   (c) $6(7 - x) \leqslant 2x \leqslant 13 - (5x + 1)$

7. The velocity v of a particle at time t is given by the formula $v = u + at$.
   (a) When $u = 18$, $v = 30$, and $t = 4$, find the value of a.
   (b) When $u = 10$ and $a = 3$, find the range of the time t such that v is greater than 16 but less than 49.

8. A family consumes $\frac{3}{10}$ kg of rice a day. If the family has 15 kg of rice, find the minimum number of days required such that the amount of rice left will be less than 4 kg.

9. A swimming club charges a monthly membership fee of $20 and an admission fee of $3 per entry. Cathy spends more than $50 on the club in a month. Find the minimum number of times she can swim in the club in a month.

10. **(a)** Factorise $3c(d - 2e) - (d - 2e)$. [1]
    (b) Solve the inequality $4k - 1 < 14 + k$. [1]
    (c) Solve the simultaneous equations
    $$y = 6x - 4,$$
    $$3x - 2y = 5.$$
    [3]
    NP1/2000/22

11. **(a)** Solve the inequality $-5 < 2x + 3 < 1$. [2]
    (b) Write down the largest integer, x, which satisfies $-5 < 2x + 3 < 1$. [1]
    NP1/2001/10

12. **(a)** Simplify $2e + 3f - 2(e + f)$. [1]
    (b) Solve the inequality $a - 2 < 4(5 - a)$. [2]
    (c) Solve the simultaneous equations
    $$x = 2y + 11,$$
    $$4x + 3y = 0.$$
    [2]
    NP1/2002/21

13. **(a)** Solve $-8 < 2x + 3 < 11$. [2]
    (b) Write down the greatest and least integers which satisfy
    $$-8 < 2x + 3 < 11.$$
    [2]
    NP1/2003/16

14. **(a)** During one week the temperatures at midnight were
    $$3\,°C, 4.5\,°C, 1\,°C, -2\,°C, 0\,°C, -6.5\,°C, -3.5\,°C.$$
    Find the difference between the highest and lowest temperatures.
    [1]
    (b) Find all the integers which satisfy both
    $$2x + 7 < 3 \text{ and } x \geqslant -4.$$
    [1]
    NP1/2004/10

Extend Your Learning Curve

Purchasing Power

Mrs Foo plans to spend not more than $39 on fish and chickens from a supermarket. The price of a fish is $7 and the price of a chicken is $5. How many combinations of different numbers of fish and chickens can she buy? Assume that the fish and chickens are bought whole. (Suggestion: Make a list or draw a table.)

Write In Your Journal

Write down how you can apply inequalities to some situations in your daily life. A possible application would be the planning of your monthly expenditure and savings.

4 Conditions Of Congruence And Similarity

If you are a judge in a sailing race, you will have to ascertain that all the triangular sails of the sailing boats are identical. Without taking down the sails from their masts, how would you determine whether the sails on each of the boats are of the same shape and size?

Let's learn to...

- state the conditions for two triangles to be congruent
- identify congruent triangles
- state the conditions for two triangles to be similar
- identify similar triangles
- determine whether two plane figures or solids are similar
- state the relationship between the ratio of areas and the ratio of lengths of two similar plane figures
- state the relationship between the ratio of volumes and the ratio of lengths of two similar solids
- apply the above properties to solve problems

4.1 Congruent Triangles

A. Side-Side-Side Congruence

In Secondary 2, we learnt that two polygons are **congruent** if they have the same shape and size.

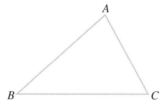 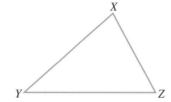

We shall take a closer look at the congruence of a special class of polygons: triangles. Consider the two triangles in the above diagram. If we trace $\triangle ABC$ on a piece of paper and place it over $\triangle XYZ$, we will find that the two triangles coincide. That means,

$$\angle A = \angle X,$$
$$\angle B = \angle Y,$$
$$\angle C = \angle Z,$$
$$AB = XY,$$
$$BC = YZ,$$
$$CA = ZX.$$

Therefore, $\triangle ABC$ is congruent to $\triangle XYZ$. We denote this by

$$\triangle ABC \equiv \triangle XYZ \; (\equiv \text{ is read as 'is congruent to').}$$

The above pairs of equal angles and equal sides are called the **corresponding angles** and **corresponding sides** of the congruent triangles respectively. We can say that:

In some books, the symbol for congruence is '≅'.

> When two triangles are congruent, each pair of corresponding angles and each pair of corresponding sides are equal.
> (Abbreviation: corr. parts of ≡ △s)

A triangle has 6 parts – 3 sides and 3 angles. To prove the congruence of two triangles, do we need to verify that all 6 parts of one triangle are equal to the corresponding parts of the other triangle? What conditions are necessary to determine their congruence?

Class Activity 1

1. In this activity, you may use a ruler, a protractor and a pair of compasses, or Geometer's Sketchpad (GSP), for your construction.

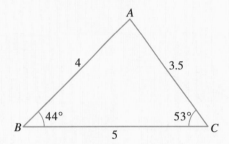

Construct six different triangles, each according to the conditions given in **(a)** to **(f)**. Label each triangle *ABC*. In each case, compare your triangle to that drawn by your nearest classmate. Are the two triangles congruent?

(a) $\angle ABC = 44°$

(b) $BC = 5$ cm

(c) $\angle ABC = 44°$ and $\angle ACB = 53°$

(d) $AB = 4$ cm and $BC = 5$ cm

(e) $\angle ABC = 44°$ and $BC = 5$ cm

(f) $AB = 4$ cm, $BC = 5$ cm and $AC = 3.5$ cm

2. From your observations of the above drawings, answer the following questions. Can two triangles be congruent if

(a) there is only one pair of equal corresponding angles,

(b) there is only one pair of equal corresponding sides,

(c) only two pairs of corresponding angles are equal,

(d) only two pairs of corresponding sides are equal,

(e) there are only one pair of equal corresponding angles and one pair of equal corresponding sides,

(f) three pairs of corresponding sides are equal?

From Class Activity 1, we cannot determine whether two triangles are congruent if only one or two corresponding parts of the two triangles are equal. However, the result in question **1(f)** does suggest the following property.

The SSS property is applied in the building and construction industry to make structures stable.

> If three pairs of corresponding sides of two triangles are equal, then the two triangles are congruent. This is also known as the Side-Side-Side test.
> (Abbreviation: SSS)

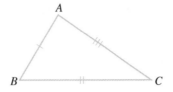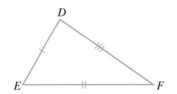

In triangles *ABC* and *DEF*,

$AB = DE$, $BC = EF$ and $AC = DF$.

∴ △*ABC* ≡ △*DEF*   (SSS)

Note: The vertices of congruent triangles must be written in a **corresponding order**.
In this case, we should write △*ABC* ≡ △*DEF*, but NOT △*ABC* ≡ △*DFE*.

Example 1 In the figure, $AB = AD$, $BC = DC$, ∠*BAC* = 45°.
(a) Show that △*ABC* ≡ △*ADC*.
(b) Find ∠*x*.

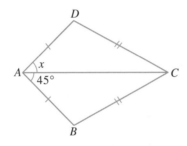

Solution **(a)** In △*ABC* and △*ADC*,

$AC = AC$,   (common side)
$AB = AD$ and $BC = DC$.   (given)

Hence, △*ABC* ≡ △*ADC*.   (SSS)

(b) ∠*DAC* = ∠*BAC*   (corr. parts of ≡ △s)
∴ ∠*x* = 45°

▶ *Try It 1!* In the figure, $AB = AC$, *M* is the midpoint of *BC* and ∠*ABM* = 60°.
(a) Show that △*ABM* ≡ △*ACM*.
(b) Find ∠*y*.

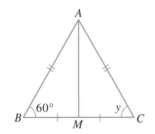

B. Side-Angle-Side and Angle-Side-Angle Congruence

Apart from SSS, are two triangles congruent if they have three corresponding parts that are equal? Let us investigate some cases to find out.

Class Activity 2

1. In this activity, you may use a ruler, protractor and a pair of compasses, or GSP, for your construction.

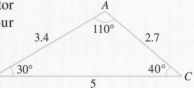

    Construct six different triangles, each according to the conditions given in **(a)** to **(e)**. Label each triangle *ABC*. In each case, determine whether your triangle is congruent to that drawn by your nearest classmate.

	Condition	Given
(a)	SAS	$AB = 3.4$ cm, $\angle ABC = 30°$, $BC = 5$ cm
(b)	ASA	$\angle ABC = 30°$, $BC = 5$ cm, $\angle ACB = 40°$
(c)	ASS (or SSA)	$\angle ABC = 30°$, $BC = 5$ cm, $AC = 2.7$ cm
(d)	AAA	$\angle BAC = 110°$, $\angle ADC = 30°$, $\angle ACB = 40°$
(e)	AAS (or SAA)	$\angle ABC = 30°$, $\angle BCA = 40°$, $AC = 2.7$ cm

2. Using GSP, open the sample file **Triangles.gsp** and find out whether each of the above conditions can guarantee the congruence of two triangles. The file may be located at the directory

    C:\ProgramFiles\Sketchpad\Samples\Sketches\Geometry.

From the above class activity, we can summarise the following two conditions for congruence of triangles.

> If two sides and the included angle of one triangle are equal to the corresponding parts of another triangle, then the two triangles are congruent. This is also known as the Side-Angle-Side test.
> (Abbreviation: SAS)

In triangles *ABC* and *DEF*,

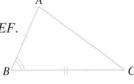
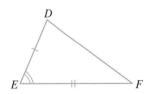

$AB = DE$, $\angle ABC = \angle DEF$ and $BC = EF$.
∴ $\triangle ABC \equiv \triangle DEF$ (SAS)

Note that in applying the SAS condition, the angle in each triangle must be **included** between the two sides. In the diagram below, the angle 30° is not included between the two known sides in each triangle. In this case (ASS case), the two triangles may not be congruent.

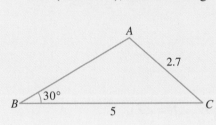
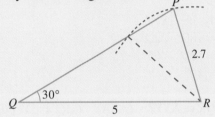

If two angles and the included side of one triangle are equal to the corresponding parts of another triangle, then the two triangles are congruent. This is also known as the Angle-Side-Angle test.
(Abbreviation: ASA)

In triangles *ABC* and *DEF*,

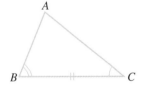

$\angle B = \angle E$, $BC = EF$ and $\angle C = \angle F$.
∴ $\triangle ABC \equiv \triangle DEF$ (ASA)

Example 2   In the figure, *AE* and *BD* bisect each other at *C*, and $AB = 5$ cm.
  (a) Name the triangle that is congruent to $\triangle ABC$.
  (b) Find the length of *DE*.

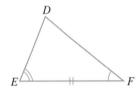

Solution   **(a)** In $\triangle ABC$ and $\triangle EDC$,

   $\angle ACB = \angle ECD$ (vert. opp. $\angle$s)
   ∴ $\triangle ABC \equiv \triangle EDC$ (SAS)   (Given $AC = CE$ and $BC = DC$.)
   i.e. $\triangle EDC$ is congruent to $\triangle ABC$.

  (b) $DE = BA$ (corr. parts of $\equiv \triangle$s)
     ∴ $DE = 5$ cm

 *Try It 2!*   In the figure, *ACE* and *BCD* are straight lines.
$AC = DC$, $BC = EC$ and $DE = 8$ cm.
  (a) Name the triangle that is congruent to $\triangle ABC$.
  (b) Find the length of *AB*.

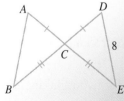

Example 3 (a) Find $\angle PRQ$ and $\angle XZY$ in the diagram.
  (b) State why $\triangle PQR$ is congruent to $\triangle XYZ$.

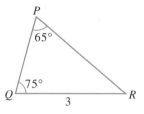
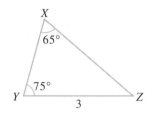

Solution (a) In $\triangle PQR$,
$$\angle PRQ = 180° - \angle P - \angle Q \quad (\angle \text{ sum of } \triangle)$$
$$= 180° - 65° - 75°$$
$$= 40°$$

Similarly, in $\triangle XYZ$,
$$\angle XZY = 180° - \angle X - \angle Y$$
$$= 180° - 65° - 75°$$
$$= 40°$$

(b) $\therefore$ $\triangle PQR \equiv \triangle XYZ$ (ASA) ($\angle Q = \angle Y$, $QR = YZ$, $\angle R = \angle Z$)

Note: This example is an example of the AAS (Angle-Angle-Side) condition. In fact, by the angle sum of triangle, when two pairs of corresponding angles of two triangles are equal, the third pair of corresponding angles of the two triangles are also equal. Therefore, the AAS condition can be considered as another variation of the ASA condition for congruence.

▶ *Try It 3!* (a) Find $\angle MLN$ and $\angle UTV$ in the diagram.
  (b) State why $\triangle LMN$ is congruent to $\triangle TUV$.

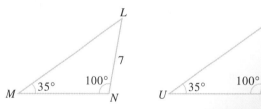

C. Right Angle-Hypotenuse-Side Congruence

Class Activity 3

1. Draw a triangle ABC in which $\angle ABC = 90°$, $BC = 2$ cm and $AC = 3$ cm, using a ruler and a pair of compasses, or GSP.

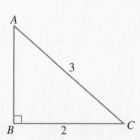

2. Determine whether your triangle is congruent to another one drawn by your nearest classmate.

3. Suggest a condition for two right-angled triangles to be congruent.

The above class activity reveals the following property.

> If the hypotenuse and one side of a right-angled triangle are equal to the corresponding parts of another right-angled triangle, then both triangles are congruent. This is also known as the Right Angle-Hypotenuse-Side test.
> (Abbreviation: RHS)

In triangles ABC and XYZ,

$\angle C = \angle Z = 90°$, $AB = XY$ and $BC = YZ$.

$\therefore \triangle ABC \equiv \triangle XYZ$ (RHS)

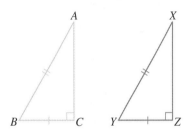

Example 4   In the figure, $XY = XZ = 8$ cm, $YZ = 6$ cm and $\angle XNZ = 90°$.

(a) Name the congruent triangles in the figure.

(b) Find YN.

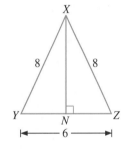

Solution   **(a)** $\angle XNY = 180° - \angle XNZ$ (adj. $\angle$s on a st. line)

$= 180° - 90°$

$= 90°$

$\therefore \triangle XYN \equiv \triangle XZN$ (RHS)   ($\angle XNY = \angle XNZ = 90°$, $XY = XZ$, XN is common)

(b) $YN = ZN$ (corr. parts of $\equiv \triangle$s)

$YN + ZN = YZ$

$\therefore \quad YN = \dfrac{1}{2} YZ$

$= \dfrac{1}{2} \times 6$

$= 3$ cm

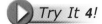 *Try It 4!*   In the figure, $AB = 7$ cm, $CD = 7$ cm, $\angle CBD = 90°$, $\angle ADB = 90°$ and $\angle BAD = 65°$.

(a) Name the congruent triangles in the figure.

(b) Find $\angle x$.

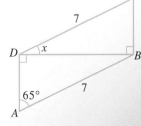

Exercise 4.1

Basic Practice

1. In each of the following, name the pair of congruent triangles and state the reason for the congruence.

(a)

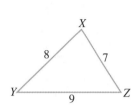

(b)

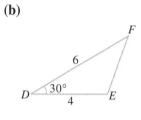 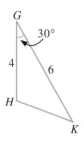

(c)

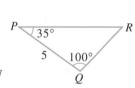 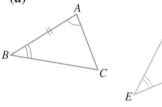

(d)

 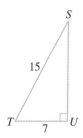 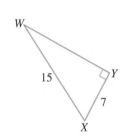

2. In each of the following, name the pair of congruent triangles and state the reason for the congruence.

(a)

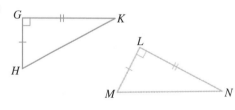

(b)

(c)

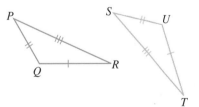

(d)

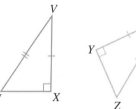

3. In each of the following, determine whether the two triangles are congruent.
    If so, state the reason.

    (a)

    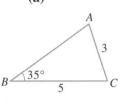
    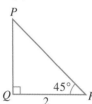

    (b)

    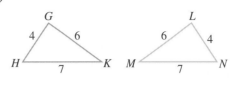

    (c)

    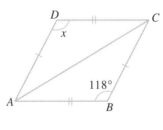

    (d)

    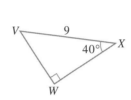
    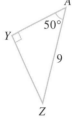

4. In each of the following diagrams,
    (i)   name the pair of congruent triangles,
    (ii) give a reason for the congruence in **(i)**,
    (iii) find the unknown angle or side marked *x*.

    (a)

    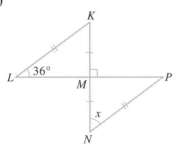

    (b)

    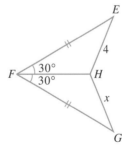

    (c)

    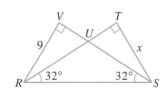

    (d)

5. Huili wants to determine the distance between two points, *A* and *B*, on the edge of a lake. First, she walks from *A* to *D* passing through *M*. Then she goes to point *B* at the lake. From point *B*, she walks to *C*, passing through *M* again. It is found that $AM = MD = 56$ m, $BM = MC = 48$ m and $CD = 64$ m.

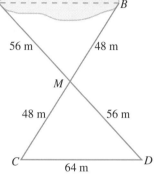

(a) Name a pair of congruent triangles in the diagram and state the reason for the congruence.

(b) Find the distance *AB*.

6.

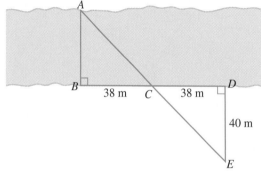

In the diagram, *A* and *B* are two spots on the opposite banks of a river. Rahmat walks along a bank from *B* to *D*, then he turns right and walks away from the bank to a point *E* such that *A*, *C* and *E* are on a straight line. $BC = DC = 38$ m and $DE = 40$ m.

(a) Write down a pair of congruent triangles in the diagram and state the reason for their congruence.

(b) Find the width of the river between *A* and *B*.

7. (a)

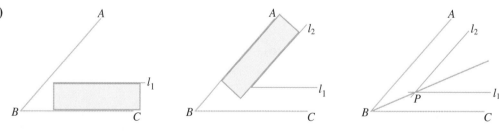

Follow the steps below to bisect $\angle ABC$ using only a straight edge.

1. Place the straight edge along *BC* and draw the line l_1.
2. Place the straight edge along *AB* and draw the line l_2.
3. Let *P* be the point of intersection of l_1 and l_2. Draw the line from *B* through *P*. Then *BP* is the angle bisector of $\angle ABC$.

(b) With the help of a protractor, check whether *BP* is the angle bisector of $\angle ABC$. Explain why *BP* is indeed the angle bisector.
(*Hint:* Consider the perpendiculars from *P* to *AB* and *BC*.)

Brainworks

8. Identify the types of quadrilaterals that can be split into two congruent triangles by one diagonal. For each type, explain why the triangles are congruent.

9. Is it possible that 5 parts of one triangle are equal to 5 parts of a second triangle even when the two triangles are not congruent? Illustrate with an example.

4.2 Similar Triangles

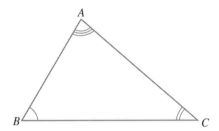
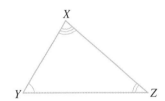

We learnt that two polygons with the same shape may have different sizes. Such polygons are called **similar polygons**. In the case of similar triangles, we have the following definition.

> Two triangles are similar if
> - each pair of corresponding angles are equal, and
> - each pair of corresponding sides are proportional.

In the above diagram,

we have   1. $\angle A = \angle X$, $\angle B = \angle Y$, $\angle C = \angle Z$,

and   2. $\dfrac{AB}{XY} = \dfrac{BC}{YZ} = \dfrac{CA}{ZX}$.

$\therefore$ $\triangle ABC$ is similar to $\triangle XYZ$.

By this definition, if two triangles are congruent, they are also similar.

Remark

A. Angle-Angle-Angle Similarity

As in the case of congruent triangles, there are some conditions that can be used to determine whether two triangles are similar. Let us explore them through the next two class activities.

Class Activity 4

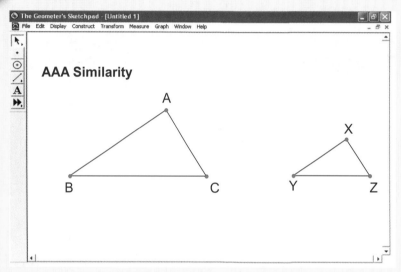

Do the following using Sketchpad.

Tasks

(a) Construct a triangle *ABC* where *BC* is horizontal.

(b) Construct a horizontal line segment *YZ*.

(c) Construct a line through *Y* and parallel to *AB*. Construct a line through *Z* and parallel to *CA*. Construct the intersecting point *X* of the above two lines.

(d) Construct the line segments *XY* and *XZ*. Hide the parallel lines drawn in **(c)**. Then a triangle *XYZ* whose angles are equal to the corresponding angles of triangle *ABC* is formed.

(e) Measure all the angles and the sides of △*ABC* and △*XYZ*.

Questions

1. Calculate the ratios of the sides *AB* : *XY*, *BC* : *YZ* and *CA* : *ZX*.

2. Drag the point *A* or *C* around and observe the variation in the numerical values of the angles and the sides of the triangles. What can you say about the angles of the two triangles? What can you say about the ratios of the sides?

Discussion: Suggest a condition for the similarity of triangles.

Class Activity 4 suggests the following property.

> If each of the three pairs of corresponding angles of two triangles are equal, then the two triangles are similar. This is also known as the Angle-Angle-Angle similarity test.

In the diagram,

$\angle A = \angle X$, $\angle B = \angle Y$ and $\angle C = \angle Z$.
$\therefore$ $\triangle ABC$ is similar to $\triangle XYZ$.

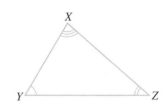

Example 5   In the figure, $AB \parallel DE$, $BC = 8$ cm, $CD = 6$ cm and $CE = 5$ cm.

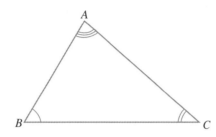

    (a) Which angle is equal to
       (i) $\angle BAC$,
       (ii) $\angle ACB$?
    (b) Name a pair of similar triangles and give the reason for the similarity.
    (c) Find the value of x.

Solution   (a) (i) $\angle BAC = \angle DEC$ (alt. $\angle$s, $AB \parallel DE$)
       (ii) $\angle ACB = \angle ECD$ (vert. opp. $\angle$s)

    (b) In $\triangle ABC$ and $\triangle EDC$,

        $\angle ABC = \angle EDC$ (alt. $\angle$s, $AB \parallel DE$)
     $\therefore$ $\triangle ABC$ is similar to $\triangle EDC$.   (three pairs of corresponding angles are equal)

    (c) $\dfrac{AC}{EC} = \dfrac{BC}{DC}$ (corr. sides of similar $\triangle$s)

        $\dfrac{x}{5} = \dfrac{8}{6}$

        $x = \dfrac{8}{6} \times 5$

         $= 6\dfrac{2}{3}$

Note: • As with congruent triangles, the vertices of similar triangles should be written in a **corresponding order**. In this example, we should <u>NOT</u> write $\triangle ABC$ is similar to $\triangle DEC$.

    • When two angles of a triangle are known, the third angle of the triangle can be found. Therefore, it is sufficient to show that two pairs of corresponding angles are equal in order to show that two triangles are similar.

▶ *Try It 5!*　In the figure, $PQ \parallel BC$, $AP = 4$ cm, $BP = 4$ cm and $BC = 6$ cm.

(a) Which angle is equal to
　(i) $\angle ABC$,
　(ii) $\angle ACB$?

(b) Name a pair of similar triangles and give the reason for the similarity.

(c) Find the value of x.

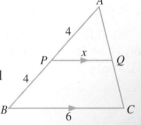

B. Side-Side-Side Similarity

Class Activity 5

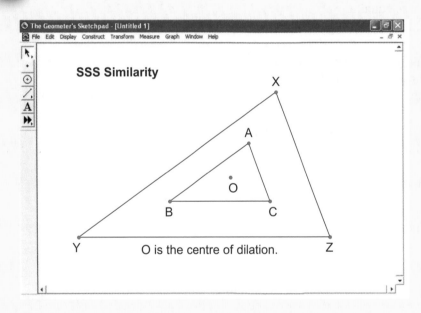

Do the following using Sketchpad.

Tasks

(a) Construct a triangle ABC.

(b) Create a point O inside the triangle and double click it to make it a centre of dilation.

(c) Select $\triangle ABC$ and dilate it to $\triangle XYZ$ using the ratio $5 : 2$.

(d) Measure all the angles and sides of $\triangle ABC$ and $\triangle XYZ$.

Questions

1. Calculate the ratios of the sides $AB : XY$, $BC : YZ$ and $CA : ZX$.

2. Drag the point A or C around and observe the variation in the numerical values of the angles and the sides of the triangles. What can you say about the three ratios of the sides? What can you say about the angles of the two triangles?

Discussion: Suggest a condition for the similarity of triangles.

The above class activity suggests the following property.

> If the three pairs of corresponding sides of two triangles are in equal proportions, then the two triangles are similar. This is also known as the Side-Side-Side similarity test.

In the diagram,

$$\frac{AB}{XY} = \frac{BC}{YZ} = \frac{CA}{ZX}.$$

∴ $\triangle ABC$ is similar to $\triangle XYZ$.

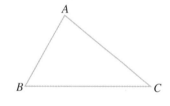

Example 6 In the diagram, $AB = 12$ cm, $BC = 18$ cm, $CA = 15$ cm, $DE = 8$ cm, $EF = 12$ cm, $FD = 10$ cm and $\angle BAC = 83°$.

    (a) Show that $\triangle ABC$ is similar to $\triangle DEF$.
    (b) Find $\angle x$.

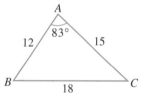

Solution   (a) $\dfrac{AB}{DE} = \dfrac{12}{8} = \dfrac{3}{2}$

            $\dfrac{BC}{EF} = \dfrac{18}{12} = \dfrac{3}{2}$

            $\dfrac{CA}{FD} = \dfrac{15}{10} = \dfrac{3}{2}$

        ∴ in $\triangle ABC$ and $\triangle DEF$,

            $\dfrac{AB}{DE} = \dfrac{BC}{EF} = \dfrac{CA}{FD}$.

      Hence, $\triangle ABC$ is similar to $\triangle DEF$.

Visit http://www.cut-the-knot.org/Curriculum/ Geometry/deVilliers.shtml to explore a game on similar triangles.

Go Online

    (b) $\angle EDF = \angle BAC$ (corr. $\angle$s of similar $\triangle$s)
        ∴ $\angle x = 83°$

Try It 6! In the diagram, $AB = 6$ cm, $BC = 9$ cm, $CA = 12$ cm, $DE = 8$ cm, $EF = 12$ cm, $FD = 16$ cm and $\angle DEF = 104°$.

(a) Show that $\triangle ABC$ is similar to $\triangle DEF$.

(b) Find $\angle y$.

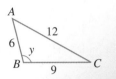
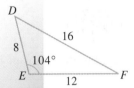

C. Side-Angle-Side Similarity

Class Activity 6

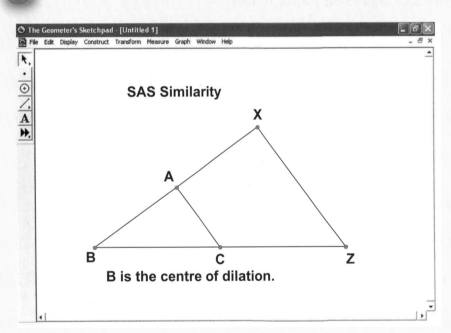

Do the following using Sketchpad.

Tasks

(a) Construct a triangle ABC.

(b) Double click the point B to make it a centre of dilation.

(c) Select $\triangle ABC$ and dilate it to $\triangle XBZ$ using the ratio $4 : 2$.

(d) Measure all the angles and sides of $\triangle ABC$ and $\triangle XBZ$.

1. Calculate the ratios of the sides $AB : XB$, $BC : BZ$ and $CA : ZX$.

2. Drag the point A or C around and observe the variation in the numerical values of the angles and the sides of the triangles. What can you say about the three ratios of the sides? What can you say about the angles of the two triangles?

Discussion: Suggest a condition for the similarity of triangles.

The above class activity suggests the following property.

> If two pairs of corresponding sides of two triangles are in equal proportions and their included angles are equal, then the two triangles are similar. This test is also known as the Side-Angle-Side similarity test.

In the diagram,

$$\frac{AB}{XY} = \frac{BC}{YZ} \text{ and } \angle B = \angle Y.$$

$\therefore$ $\triangle ABC$ is similar to $\triangle XYZ$.

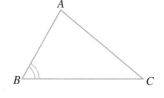
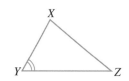

Example 7 In the diagram, $PQ = 20$ cm, $QR = 35$ cm, $RP = 30$ cm, $XY = 12$ cm, $ZX = 18$ cm, $\angle RPQ = 86°$ and $\angle ZXY = 86°$.
  (a) Show that $\triangle PQR$ is similar to $\triangle XYZ$.
  (b) Find the value of x.

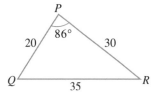
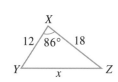

Solution (a) $\dfrac{PQ}{XY} = \dfrac{20}{12} = \dfrac{5}{3}$

$\dfrac{RP}{ZX} = \dfrac{30}{18} = \dfrac{5}{3}$

In $\triangle PQR$ and $\triangle XYZ$,

$\angle RPQ = \angle ZXY$ (given)

$\dfrac{PQ}{XY} = \dfrac{RP}{ZX}$

$\therefore$ $\triangle PQR$ is similar to $\triangle XYZ$.

(b) $\dfrac{QR}{YZ} = \dfrac{PQ}{XY}$ (corr. sides of similar $\triangle$s)

$\dfrac{35}{x} = \dfrac{20}{12}$

$\therefore$ $x = 35 \times \dfrac{12}{20} = 21$

▶ **Try It 7!**   In the diagram, $AB = 6$ cm, $BC = 4$ cm, $CA = 9$ cm, $LM = 9$ cm, $MN = 6$ cm, $\angle ABC = 127°$ and $\angle LMN = 127°$.
(a) Show that $\triangle ABC$ is similar to $\triangle LMN$.
(b) Find the value of y.

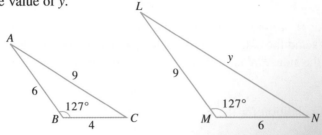

Example 8   In the diagram, $AF \parallel BE \parallel CD$, $AB = 3$ cm, $BC = 5$ cm and $AF = 2$ cm.
(a) Find the value of x.
(b) Find the value of y.

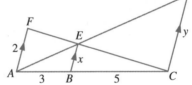

Solution   (a) $\triangle CBE$ is similar to $\triangle CAF$.   ($\angle CEB = \angle CFA$, $\angle BCE = \angle ACF$)

$$\therefore \frac{BE}{AF} = \frac{BC}{AC}$$

$$\frac{x}{2} = \frac{5}{3+5}$$

$$x = \frac{5}{4}$$

$$= 1\frac{1}{4}$$

(b) $\triangle ABE$ is similar to $\triangle ACD$.   ($\angle ABE = \angle ACD$, $\angle EAB = \angle DAC$)

$$\therefore \frac{BE}{CD} = \frac{AB}{AC}$$

$$\frac{\frac{5}{4}}{y} = \frac{3}{8}$$

$$\therefore \quad y = \frac{5}{4} \times \frac{8}{3} = 3\frac{1}{3}$$

▶ **Try It 8!**   In the diagram, $AF \parallel BE \parallel CD$, $AB = 30$ cm, $BC = 15$ cm and $CD = 10$ cm. Find the values of x and y.

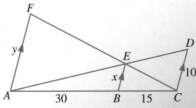

Exercise 4.2

Basic Practice

1. In each of the following, name the pair of similar triangles and state the reason for the similarity.

   (a)

   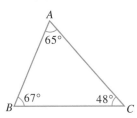

   (b)

   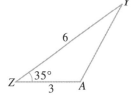

   (c)

   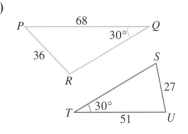

   (d)

   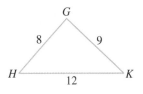

2. In each of the following, determine whether the two triangles are similar. If they are, give the reason for the similarity.

   (a)

   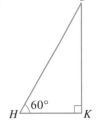

   (b)

   (c)

   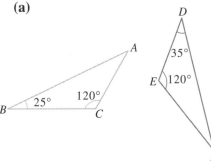

   (d)

   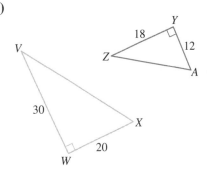

Further Practice

3. In each of the following,
   (i) name a pair of similar triangles and state the reason for the similarity,
   (ii) find the unknown x.

(a)

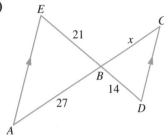

(b)

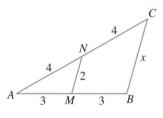

(c)

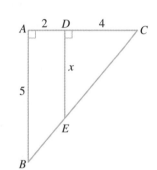

(d)

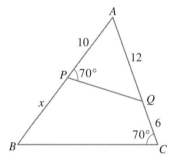

4. In the figure, $DE \parallel FG \parallel BC$, $AD = 4$ cm, $FB = 2$ cm,
   $DE = 2\frac{2}{3}$ cm, $BC = 6$ cm, $DF = x$ cm and $FG = y$ cm.
   (a) State the reason that $\triangle ADE$ is similar to $\triangle ABC$.
   (b) Find the value of x.
   (c) Find the value of y.

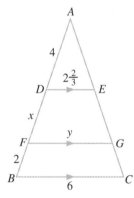

5. In the figure, $AF \parallel BE \parallel CD$, $AB = 20$ cm, $BC = 30$ cm,
   $AF = 25$ cm, $BE = x$ cm and $CD = y$ cm.
   (a) Name a triangle that is similar to $\triangle ACF$. State the
   reason for the similarity.
   (b) Find the value of x.
   (c) Find the value of y.

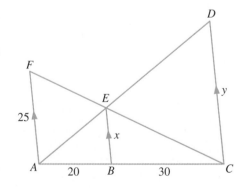

6. In the figure, *AD* // *FG*, *EF* = 12 cm, *BC* = 18 cm, *AD* = 12 cm and *FG* = *x* cm.
   (a) Name two pairs of similar triangles in the figure.
   (b) Find the ratio *AF* : *FC*.
   (c) Find the value of *x*.

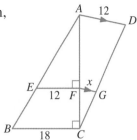

Maths@Work

7.

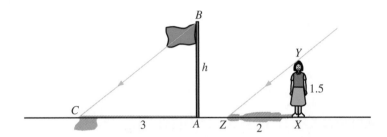

In the diagram, a girl 1.5 m tall stands in front of a vertical flag pole. The lengths of the shadows of the girl and the pole on the horizontal ground are 2 m and 3 m respectively. Find the height of the pole.

8.

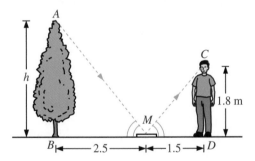

Wenrong places a plane mirror on level ground to determine the height of a tree (see the diagram). He stands at a certain distance so that he can see the top of the tree reflected from the mirror. Wenrong's eye level is 1.8 m above the ground. The distances of Wenrong and the tree from the mirror are 1.5 m and 2.5 m respectively.
   (a) Name two similar triangles in the diagram and state the reason for the similarity.
   (b) Find the height of the tree.

9. In the diagram, *PQ* is the distance across a river. In order to determine it, Lily walks along the paths *QRS* and *ST*. *T* is a spot such that *P*, *R* and *T* are on a straight line. *QR* = 30 m, *RS* = 20 m and *ST* = 12 m.
   (a) Name two similar triangles in the diagram and state the reason for the similarity.
   (b) Find the distance *PQ*.

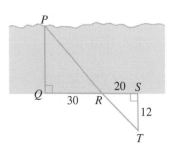

10. (a) In the diagram, *AB // CD // EF // GH*. *PQRS* and *PTUV* are straight lines such that *PQ = QR = RS*. What can you say about the lengths of *PT*, *TU* and *UV*?

(b) Using only a straight edge and a pair of compasses, divide a line segment into 3 equal parts.

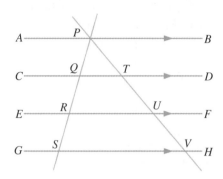

11. In △*ABC* and △*DEF*, it is given that *AB = DE*, *BC = EF* and ∠*BCA* = ∠*EFD*. Investigate whether △*ABC* is similar to △*DEF*. Give an example to support your investigation.

4.3 Ratio Of Areas Of Similar Plane Figures

We know that when two plane figures are similar, their corresponding sides are proportional. That means each pair of the corresponding sides has a ratio *k*, which is a constant. Is there any relationship between the ratio of the areas of two similar figures and *k*?

Class Activity 7

In this activity, the unit of length is cm. Copy and complete the following table.

Similar plane figures	Ratio of sides	Ratio of areas
Triangles (triangle with 8, 10; triangle with 16, 20)	Ratio of bases = ☐ = ☐	Ratio of areas = ☐ = ☐
Squares (square 12; square 18)	Ratio of sides = ☐ = ☐	Ratio of areas = ☐ = ☐

Similar plane figures	Ratio of sides	Ratio of areas
Rectangles 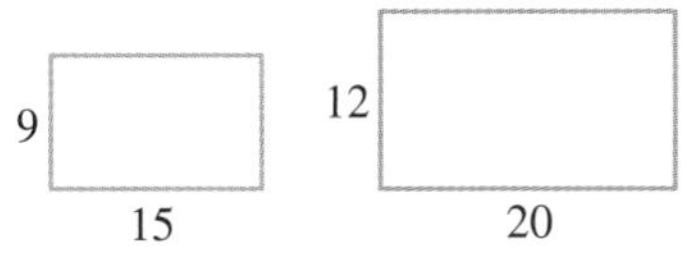	Ratio of breadths = =	Ratio of areas = =
Circles 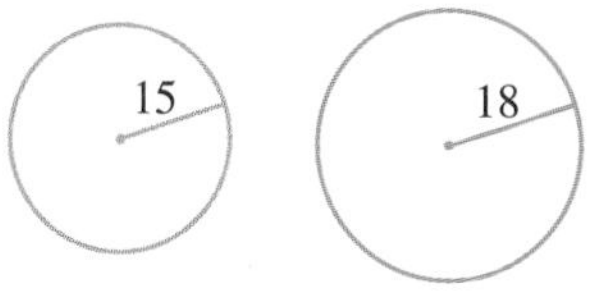	Ratio of radii = =	Ratio of areas = =
Octagons 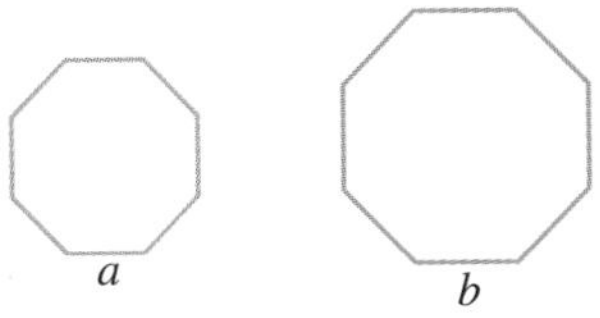	Ratio of sides $= a : b$	Ratio of areas =

From the above class activity, we can visualise the following:

> For two similar plane figures,
> if the ratio of their corresponding sides is $a : b$,
> then the ratio of their areas is $a^2 : b^2$.

Example 9 In the diagram, $DE \,//\, BC$, $AD = 12$ cm, $DB = 6$ cm and the area of $\triangle ADE = 84$ cm^2. Find

(a) the ratio of the areas of $\triangle ADE$ and $\triangle ABC$,

(b) the area of $\triangle ABC$,

(c) the area of $BCED$.

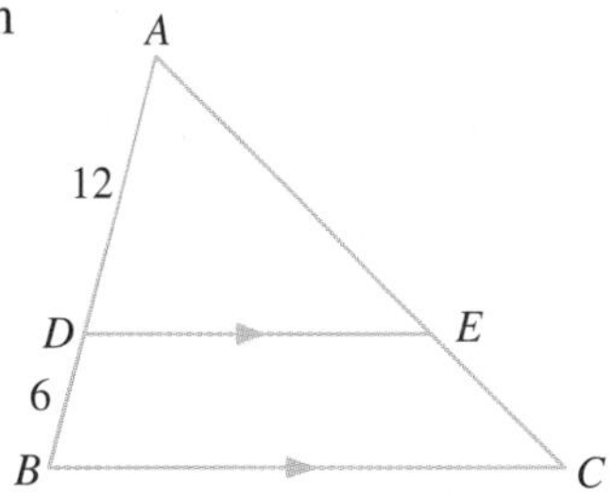

Solution   **(a)** $\triangle ADE$ is similar to $\triangle ABC$.

$\therefore$ area of $\triangle ADE$: area of $\triangle ABC = AD^2 : AB^2$

$= 12^2 : (12 + 6)^2$

$= 144 : 324$

$= 4 : 9$

(b) $\therefore$ $\dfrac{84}{\text{area of } \triangle ABC} = \dfrac{4}{9}$

Area of $\triangle ABC = 84 \times \dfrac{9}{4}$

$= 189 \text{ cm}^2$

(c)   Area of $BCED$ = area of $\triangle ABC$ – area of $\triangle ADE$

$= 189 - 84$

$= 105 \text{ cm}^2$

▶ *Try It 9!*

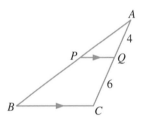

In the diagram, $PQ \parallel BC$, $AQ = 4$ cm, $QC = 6$ cm and the area of $\triangle ABC = 37.5 \text{ cm}^2$. Find

(a) the ratio $AQ : AC$,

(b) the ratio of the areas of $\triangle APQ$ and $\triangle ABC$,

(c) the area of $\triangle APQ$,

(d) the area of $BCQP$.

Example 10   The areas of two regular pentagons are 49 cm^2 and 81 cm^2. Find the ratio of the corresponding sides of these two pentagons.

Solution   Let $a : b$ be the ratio of the corresponding sides.

Since the two regular pentagons are similar to each other,

$\therefore$ $a^2 : b^2$ = ratio of their areas

$= 49 : 81$

$a : b = \sqrt{49} : \sqrt{81}$

$= 7 : 9$

▶ *Try It 10!*   The areas of two regular hexagons are 25 cm^2 and 64 cm^2. Find the ratio of the corresponding sides of these two hexagons.

Exercise 4.3

Basic Practice

1. In each of the following pairs of similar figures, find the unknown area A_1 or A_2. The units of length and area are cm and cm² respectively.

(a)

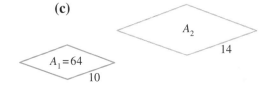

(b)

(c)

(d)

(e)

(f)

2. In each of the following pairs of similar figures, find the unknown side x. The unit of length is cm.

(a)

(b)

(c)

(d)

3. The diagonals of two squares are 2 cm and 4 cm. Find the ratio of the
   (a) perimeters of the two squares,
   (b) areas of the two squares.

4. The radii of two circles are 14 cm and 21 cm. Find the ratio of
   (a) the circumferences of the two circles,
   (b) the areas of the two circles.

5. The area of a quadrilateral with sides 6 cm, 8 cm, 7 cm and 5 cm is 40 cm^2.
   Find the area of a similar quadrilateral whose longest side is 6 cm.

6. In the diagram, AC and ED intersect at B, $AB = 20$ cm, $BC = 15$ cm, $DB = 18$ cm, $BE = 24$ cm, and the area of $\triangle ABE = 208$ cm^2.
   (a) Name a pair of similar triangles and state the reason for the similarity.
   (b) Find the area of $\triangle BCD$.

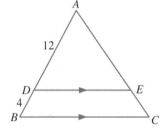

7. In the diagram, $DE \parallel BC$, $AD = 12$ cm, $BD = 4$ cm and the area of $\triangle ADE$ is 63 cm^2.
   (a) State the reason that $\triangle ADE$ is similar to $\triangle ABC$.
   (b) Find the area of $\triangle ABC$.
   (c) Find the area of $BCED$.

8. In the diagram, $AE \parallel BD$ and $BD = 15$ cm. The area of $\triangle BCD = 150$ cm^2 and the area of $ABDE = 144$ cm^2.
   (a) Find the ratio $AB : BC$.
   (b) Find the length of AE.

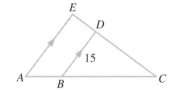

9. Two rectangular lawns, A and B, measure 50 m by 40 m and 75 m by 60 m respectively.
   (a) Show that lawn A and lawn B are similar.
   (b) Find the ratio of
      (i) the diagonals of A and B,
      (ii) the areas of A and B.
   (c) It takes 20 minutes to mow lawn A. Assume the rate of mowing is the same, how much time will it take to mow lawn B?

10. The diagram shows the face of a cake. The inner heart is filled with strawberry and is surrounded by a chocolate border of uniform width such that the inner heart is similar to the outer heart of the cake. The heights of the inner and outer hearts are 10 cm and 18 cm respectively. The area of the inner heart is 50 cm². Find the area of the chocolate border.

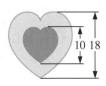

11.

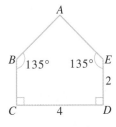

The diagram shows the vertical cross-section of a hut. The base *CD* is 4 m wide and the wall *DE* is 2 m high.
(a) Find ∠*BAE*.
(b) Find the height of the hut (i.e. the perpendicular distance from *A* to *CD*).
(c) Find the area of this cross-section.
(d) A similar hut has a base of 3 m in width. Find the area of its vertical cross-section.

(**Brainworks**)

12.

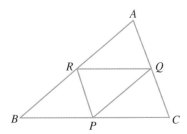

(a) In the diagram, *P*, *Q* and *R* are the midpoints of the sides of △*ABC*. Show that
   (i)   △*PQR* is similar to △*ABC*,
   (ii) area of △*PQR* = $\frac{1}{4}$ area of △*ABC*.
(b) Can the conclusions in (a) be extended to a quadrilateral *ABCD*? That is, if *P*, *Q*, *R* and *S* are the midpoints of the sides of *ABCD*,
   (i)   is *PQRS* similar to *ABCD*?
   (ii) is the area of *PQRS* equal to $\frac{1}{4}$ of the area of *ABCD*?

4.4 Ratio Of Volumes Of Similar Solids

When two solids are similar, they have the same shape and each pair of their corresponding sides has a constant ratio k. How are the ratio of their surface areas and the ratio of their volumes related to k?

Class Activity 8

In this activity, the unit of length is cm. Copy and complete the following table.

Similar solids	Ratio of sides	Ratio of volumes
Cubes 5 10	Ratio of sides = ▢ = ▢	Ratio of volumes = ▢ = ▢
Square pyramids 6 9 4 6	Ratio of sides = ▢ = ▢	Ratio of volumes = ▢ = ▢
Cylinders 9 15 6 10	Ratio of sides = ▢ = ▢	Ratio of volumes = ▢ = ▢
Spheres a b	Ratio of radii = ▢	Ratio of volumes = ▢ = ▢

From Class Activity 8, we can visualise the following:

> For two similar solids,
> if the ratio of their corresponding sides is $a : b$,
> then the ratio of their volumes is $a^3 : b^3$.

Since the corresponding faces of two similar solids are similar figures, we can extend the property of the ratio of areas of similar plane figures to the ratio of areas of corresponding plane faces of similar solids.

Example 11　The ratio of the base areas of two similar solid copper cylinders is 9 : 16.
(a) Find the ratio of the radii of the bases of the cylinders.
(b) Find the ratio of the volumes of the cylinders.
(c) If the mass of the smaller cylinder is 540 g, find the mass of the larger cylinder.

Test your 3-D visualisation skill at this website http://www.cut-the-knot.org/Curriculum/Geometry/CubeIllusion.shtml where two cubes create a visual illusion.

Solution　(a) Let r cm and R cm be the radii of the bases of the cylinders.

Then,　ratio of base areas $= r^2 : R^2$
$$r^2 : R^2 = 9 : 16$$
$$r : R = \sqrt{9} : \sqrt{16}$$
$$= 3 : 4$$

(b) Ratio of volumes $= r^3 : R^3$
$$= 3^3 : 4^3$$
$$= 27 : 64$$

(c) The mass of a cylinder is proportional to its volume.

$\therefore$ $\dfrac{\text{mass of smaller cylinder}}{\text{mass of larger cylinder}} = \dfrac{\text{volume of smaller cylinder}}{\text{volume of larger cylinder}}$

$$\dfrac{540}{\text{mass of larger cylinder}} = \dfrac{27}{64}$$

mass of larger cylinder $= 540 \times \dfrac{64}{27}$
$$= 1280 \text{ g}$$

▶ *Try It 11!*　The ratio of the areas of the corresponding faces of two crystal cubes is 25 : 49.
(a) Find the ratio of the corresponding sides of the cubes.
(b) Find the ratio of the volumes of the cubes.
(c) If the mass of the larger cube is 686 g, find the mass of the smaller cube.

Example 12 The diagram shows a cup in the form of an inverted cone of height 18 cm and base radius 7.5 cm. It is filled with water to a depth of 12 cm.

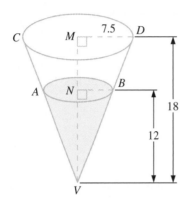

(a) Find the radius of the water surface.
(b) Find the volume of water in the cup.
(c) Find the additional volume of water required to fill up the cup.
Express your answers in terms of π where applicable.

Solution (a) In the diagram,
$\triangle VNB$ is similar to $\triangle VMD$.

$$\therefore \quad \frac{NB}{MD} = \frac{VN}{VM}$$

$$\frac{NB}{7.5} = \frac{12}{18}$$

$$NB = 5 \text{ cm}$$

i.e. the radius of the water surface is 5 cm.

(b) Volume of water $= \dfrac{1}{3} \pi \times NB^2 \times VN$

$$= \frac{1}{3} \pi \times 5^2 \times 12$$

$$= 100\pi \text{ cm}^3$$

(c) $\dfrac{\text{Volume of water}}{\text{Volume of the cup}} = \left(\dfrac{12}{18}\right)^3$

$$\therefore \quad \frac{100\pi}{\text{Volume of the cup}} = \frac{8}{27}$$

Volume of the cup $= 337.5\pi \text{ cm}^3$

$\therefore$ the required volume of water $= 337.5\pi - 100\pi$
$$= 237.5\pi \text{ cm}^3$$

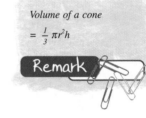

Volume of a cone

$= \frac{1}{3}\pi r^2 h$

Remark

▶ *Try It 12!* The diagram shows a frustum formed by cutting off a small cone *VCD* from the cone *VAB* of height 8 cm. The radii of the upper and lower bases of the frustum are 3 cm and 6 cm respectively. Find
(a) the length of *MN*,
(b) the volume of the small cone *VCD*,
(c) the volume of the frustum.
Express your answers in terms of π where applicable.

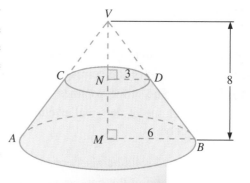

Exercise 4.4

Basic Practice

1. In each of the following pairs of similar solids, find the unknown volume V_1 or V_2. (The unit of length is cm and the unit of volume is cm³.)

    (a)

    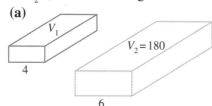

    (b)

    (c)

    (d)

    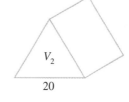

2. Copy and complete the following table for the ratios of measures of similar solids.

	Ratio of sides	Ratio of areas of corresponding plane faces	Ratio of volumes
(a)	1 : 2		
(b)		4 : 9	
(c)			125 : 216

Further Practice

3. The ratio of the areas of corresponding faces of two cubes is 49 : 36.
   (a) Find the ratio of the corresponding sides of the two cubes.
   (b) Find the ratio of the volumes of the two cubes.
   (c) If the volume of the smaller cube is 648 cm^3, find the volume of the larger cube.

4. The radii of two solid hemispheres are in the ratio 2 : 3.
   (a) Find the ratio of the base areas of the two hemispheres.
   (b) Find the ratio of the volumes of the two hemispheres.
   (c) If the base area of the larger one is 540 cm^2, find the base area of the smaller one.

5. A pentagonal prism is 25 cm high and its base area is 170 cm^2.
   (a) Find the volume of the prism.
   (b) A similar prism is 30 cm high. Find its
      (i) base area,
      (ii) volume.

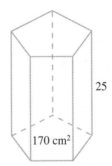

6. The diagram shows two similar solids, made of the same material, whose base areas are in the ratio 25 : 49. The base area of the larger one is 147 cm^2.
   (a) Find the base area of the smaller one.
   (b) What is the ratio of the heights of the two solids?
   (c) If the mass of the smaller solid is 8.25 kg, find the mass of the larger solid.

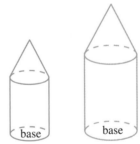

Maths@Work

7. Two similar statues, made of the same material, are of heights 15 cm and 20 cm. The mass of the smaller one is 405 g. Find the mass of the larger one.

8. A cup is in the form of an inverted square pyramid. When the depth of water is 10 cm, the volume of water is 187.5 cm^3. When x cm^3 of water is poured into the cup, the water level rises to 14 cm.
   (a) Find the value of x.
   (b) Find the increase in the area of the water surface in the cup.

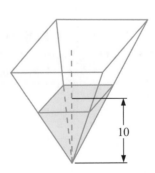

9. The heights of three similar solid metal cylinders are 6 cm, 8 cm and 10 cm respectively.

    (a) Find the ratio of the base areas of the cylinders.

    (b) Find the ratio of the volumes of the cylinders.

    (c) If the cylinders are melted and recast into one similar cylinder, find the height of the cylinder formed.

10.

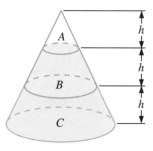

A carpenter cuts a wooden cone into three parts A, B and C by two planes parallel to the base as shown in the diagram. The heights of the three parts are equal.

    (a) Find the ratio of the volumes of parts A, B and C.

    (b) Find the ratio of the base areas of parts A, B and C.

    (c) If the volume of the original cone is 540 cm^3, find the volume of part B.

    Brainworks

11.

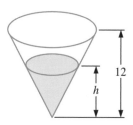

There are some paper cups at a drinking fountain. Each cup is in the form of an inverted cone of height 12 cm. Determine a method, mathematical or non-mathematical, to find the water level h cm such that the volume of water is half of the capacity of the cup.

4

In A Nutshell

Conditions for Congruent Triangles

1. SSS (Side-Side-Side)
2. SAS (Side-Angle-Side)
3. ASA (Angle-Side-Angle)
4. RHS (Right angle-Hypotenuse-Side)

Conditions for Similar Triangles

1. Angle-Angle-Angle similarity
2. Side-Side-Side similarity
3. Side-Angle-Side similarity

Ratio of Areas of Similar Plane Figures

If the ratio of sides is $a : b$,

then the ratio of areas is $a^2 : b^2$.

Ratio of Volumes of Similar Solids

If the ratio of sides is $a : b$,

then the ratio of volumes is $a^3 : b^3$.

Revision Exercise 4

1. In each of the following, name two triangles which are congruent and state the reason for the congruence.

   (a)
   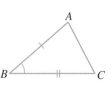
   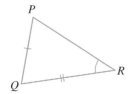
   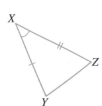

   (b)
   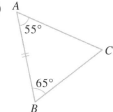
   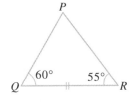
   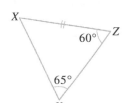

   (c)
   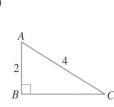
   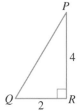
   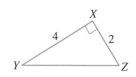

2. In each of the following, name a pair of congruent triangles and give a reason for the congruence.

   (a)
   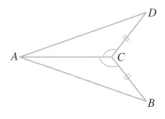

   (b)
   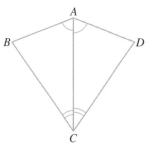

   (c)
   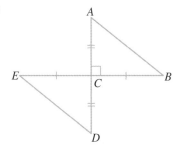

   (d)
   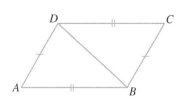

3. In the figure, *ABCD* is a rectangle, *EF* passes through the intersecting point, *M*, of the diagonals *AC* and *BD*.

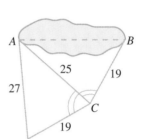

   (a) Is △*ADM* congruent to △*CBM*?
   (b) Name the triangle that is congruent to △*AEM* and state the reason for the congruence.
   (c) Name another pair of the congruent triangles in the figure.

4. Minghua determines the distance between two points, *A* and *B*, of a pond by taking some measurements on land as shown in the diagram. *BC* = 19 m, *AC* = 25 m, *CD* = 19 m, *AD* = 27 m and ∠*ACB* = ∠*ACD*.

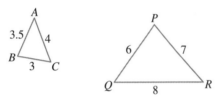

   (a) Name a pair of congruent triangles and state the reason for the congruence.
   (b) Find the distance *AB*.

5. In each of the following, write down a pair of triangles which are similar.
   (a)

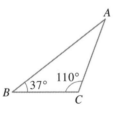

   (b)

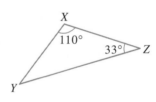

   (c)

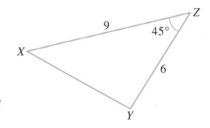

6. In each of the following, write down a pair of similar triangles and find the unknown *x*.
   (a)

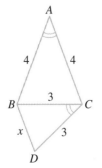

   (b)

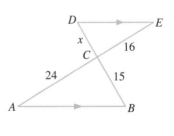

110

(c)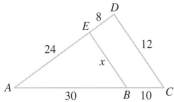

(d)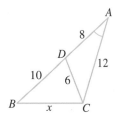

7. In the diagram, $\angle ABE = \angle CBD$, $AE = 12$ cm, $BC = 17$ cm and $CD = 8$ cm.
   (a) Name a pair of similar triangles and state the reason for the similarity.
   (b) Find the length of
      (i) BD,
      (ii) DE,
      (iii) AB.

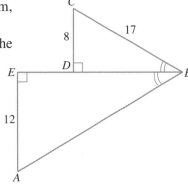

8. In the diagram, $\angle ADC = \angle BAC = 90°$, $BD = 4$ cm and $DC = 9$ cm.
   (a) Show that $\triangle ABD$ is similar to $\triangle CAD$.
   (b) Find the length of AD.
   (c) Find the length of AC.
   (d) Find the area of $\triangle ABD$.

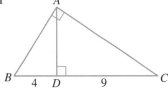

9. In the diagram, $PQ \parallel BC$, $QR \parallel AB$, $AP = 8$ cm, $PB = 6$ cm, $PQ = 10$ cm and the area of $\triangle APQ = 36$ cm^2.
   (a) Show that $\triangle APQ$ is similar to $\triangle ABC$.
   (b) Find the length of BC.
   (c) Find the area of $\triangle ABC$.
   (d) Find the length of RC.
   (e) Find the area of
      (i) $\triangle RCQ$,
      (ii) $BRQP$.

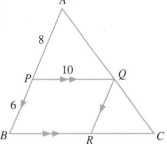

10. The volumes of two similar cylinders are in the ratio $343 : 729$.
   (a) Find the ratio of the base radii of the cylinders.
   (b) Find the ratio of the base areas of the cylinders.

11. The ratio of the areas of the corresponding plane faces of two similar right square pyramids, made of the same material, is $16 : 25$.
   (a) Find the ratio of the heights of the pyramids.
   (b) If the mass of the bigger pyramid is 400 g, find the mass of the smaller one.

12. The diagram shows a cup in the form of an inverted cone of base radius 7 cm and height 24 cm. It contains water to a depth of 12 cm.

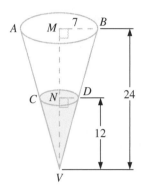

(a) Find the volume of the cup.

(b) Find the volume of water in the cup.

(c) Find the additional volume of water required in order to increase the depth of water to 18 cm.

(You may leave your answers in terms of π.)

13. In the diagram, *ABCD* is a quadrilateral with *BA* parallel to *CD*. *AC* and *BD* meet at *X* where *CX* = 8 cm and *XA* = 10 cm.

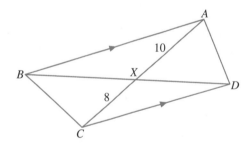

(a) Given that *BD* = 27 cm, find the length *BX*. [2]

(b) Find the ratio area of triangle *BXC* : area of triangle *AXD*. [2]

NP1/2000/17

14. The ratio of the **areas** of the bases of two geometrically similar buckets is 4 : 9.

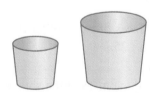

(a) The **area** of the top of the smaller bucket is 480 cm². What is the **area** of the top of the larger bucket? [1]

(b) **Write down** the ratio of the **heights** of the two buckets. [1]

(c) Both buckets are filled with sand. The **mass** of sand in the larger bucket is 36 kg.

Find the **mass** of sand in the smaller bucket. [2]

NP1/2001/18

15. *ABCD* is a rectangle. *ABP* and *BCQ* are equilateral triangles.
    (a) Prove that $\angle PBQ = 90°$. [1]

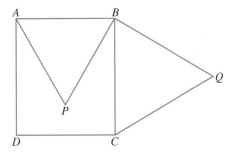

(b) By proving that two triangles are congruent, show that *AC = PQ*. Give reasons for each of your statements. [3]

NP1/2003/17

16. In the diagram, $\angle ABC = \angle AED$.

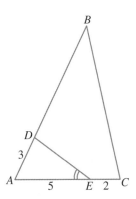

(a) Explain why triangles *ABC* and *AED* are similar. [1]
(b) Given also that *AD* = 3 cm, *AE* = 5 cm and *EC* = 2 cm, calculate
    (i) *BD*, [3]
    (ii) $\dfrac{\text{Area of triangle } AED}{\text{Area of triangle } ABC}$. [1]

NP1/2003/21

17. *ABCD* is a rectangle and *M* is a point on *CD*. *AC* and *BM* meet at *X*.

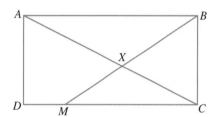

(a) Prove that triangles *CXM* and *AXB* are similar.

Answer (a) In triangles *CXM* and *AXB*,

. . . .

. . . .

. . . .

. . . . [2]

(b) It is given that *CM* = 3*MD*.
Find the ratio
   (i) area of $\triangle CXM$: area of $\triangle AXB$, [1]
   (ii) area of $\triangle BXC$: area of rectangle *ABCD*. [1]

NP1/2004/18

Extend Your Learning Curve

Sierpinski Triangle

$n = 1$ $n = 2$ $n = 3$ $n = 4$

In the above diagram, we construct a series of triangular patterns. We begin with a blue equilateral triangle ($n = 1$). Join the midpoint of each side to form four separate triangles, and remove the triangle in the centre (see the figure for $n = 2$). For each of the remaining three triangles, we perform the same trick to get the figures for $n = 3$ and $n = 4$. Continuing this way, we will get a series of triangles called **Sierpinski Triangle**.

(a) Complete the following table.

n	1	2	3	4
Number of blue triangles	1			
Area of one blue triangle	1			
Total blue area	1			

(b) Suggest a formula for the number of blue triangles at the nth stage.

(c) Suggest a formula for the area of one blue triangle at the nth stage.

(d) Suggest a formula for the total blue area at the nth stage.

(e) What happens to the total blue area when n becomes very large?

Go online to visit these websites for an interactive Sierpinski Triangle demonstration.

(i) http://math.rice.edu/~lanius/fractals/sierjava.html

(ii) http://www.shodor.org/interactivate/activities/gasket/

Write In Your Journal

Do you use congruent or similar shapes in your daily life? Give some examples.

5 Functions And Graphs

A designer wants to have a rectangular poster of area 4 m². Suppose the dimensions of the poster are x m by y m. What is the relationship between x and y? Can you draw the graph of the relationship?

Let's learn to...

- sketch the graphs of quadratic functions of the forms $y = \pm(x - h)^2 + k$ and $y = \pm(x - p)(x - q)$
- draw the graph of the function $y = ax^n$ for $n = -2, -1, 0, 1, 2$ and 3
- draw the graph of the sum of not more than 3 functions of the form $y = ax^n$ for $n = -2, -1, 0, 1, 2$ and 3
- draw the graph of an exponential function $y = ka^x$ where a is a positive integer
- estimate the gradient of a curve by drawing a tangent to the curve

5.1 Graph Sketching Of Quadratic Functions

In Secondary Two, we learnt how to draw a quadratic graph of the form $y = ax^2 + bx + c$ by plotting some points and then joining them by a smooth curve. We have also learnt that the basic forms of a quadratic graph are $y = x^2$ and $y = -x^2$. In both $y = x^2$ and $y = -x^2$, the line of symmetry is $x = 0$ and the turning point is at the origin $(0, 0)$. The diagrams below illustrate the sketches of these two graphs.

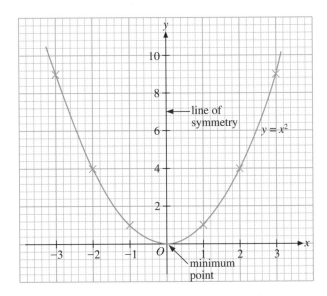

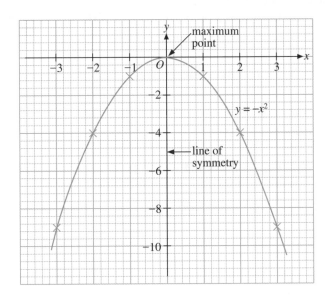

We shall now consider another form of quadratic graphs which can be expressed as $y = \pm(x - h)^2 + k$, where h and k are constants.

A. Graph of $y = \pm(x - h)^2 + k$

Class Activity 1

Let us explore some quadratic graphs in the form $y = (x - h)^2 + k$ or $y = -(x - h)^2 + k$, where h and k are constants, using Sketchpad.

1.
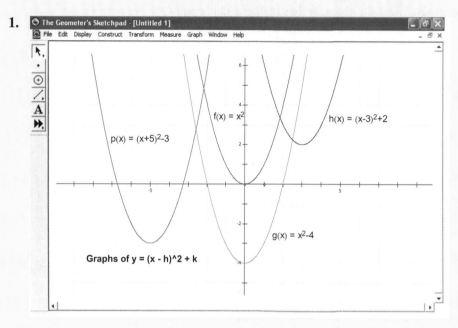

(a) Select the menu **Graph | Plot New Function**. A **New Function** window will appear. Enter x^2 in the function input area and then click **OK** (^2 means to the power 2). The graph of $y = x^2$ will appear on the sketch area with grid lines.

(b) Similarly, draw the graphs of $y = x^2 - 4$, $y = (x - 3)^2 + 2$ and $y = (x + 5)^2 - 3$ on the same coordinate plane.

(c) Study the graphs, copy and complete the following table. Then consider the graph of $y = (x - h)^2 + k$, where h and k are constants.

Function	Line of symmetry	Turning point	Is the turning point maximum or minimum?
$y = x^2$	$x = 0$	$(0, 0)$	Minimum
$y = x^2 - 4$			
$y = (x - 3)^2 + 2$			
$y = (x + 5)^2 - 3$			
$y = (x - h)^2 + k$			

Sketchpad uses the notations such as f(x), g(x), ..., to denote functions.

Remark

2.

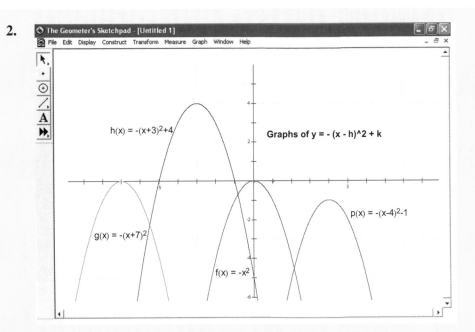

(a) Open a new window in GSP.

(b) Draw the graphs of $y = -x^2$, $y = -(x + 7)^2$, $y = -(x + 3)^2 + 4$ and $y = -(x - 4)^2 - 1$ on the same coordinate plane.

(c) Study the graphs, copy and complete the following table. Then consider the graph of $y = -(x - h)^2 + k$, where h and k are constants.

Function	Line of symmetry	Turning point	Is the turning point maximum or minimum?
$y = -x^2$	$x = 0$	$(0, 0)$	Maximum
$y = -(x + 7)^2$			
$y = -(x + 3)^2 + 4$			
$y = -(x - 4)^2 - 1$			
$y = -(x - h)^2 + k$			

The results in the above class activity can be summarised as follows:

Graph of $y = (x - h)^2 + k$	Graph of $y = -(x - h)^2 + k$
1. It has the same shape as the graph of $y = x^2$.	1. It has the same shape as the graph of $y = -x^2$.
2. It opens upwards.	2. It opens downwards.
3. Its minimum point is at the point (h, k).	3. Its maximum point is at the point (h, k).
4. The line $x = h$ is its line of symmetry.	4. The line $x = h$ is its line of symmetry.

Example 1   Sketch the graph of $y = (x - 1)^2 + 2$.

Solution   First, we gather some information before sketching the graph.
For the graph of $y = (x - 1)^2 + 2$, $h = 1$ and $k = 2$.
$\therefore$ its minimum point is (1, 2).
   The line of symmetry is the line $x = 1$.

Also, when $x = 0$, $y = (0 - 1)^2 + 2 = 3$.
$\therefore$ the graph cuts the y-axis at (0, 3).

Using the above information, we can sketch the graph of
$y = (x - 1)^2 + 2$ as shown below.

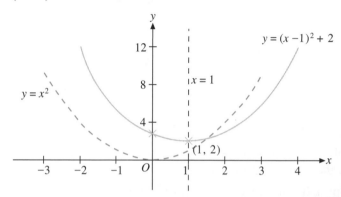

Note: • To sketch a graph, we need not use graph paper.

   • The graph of $y = (x - 1)^2 + 2$ may be obtained by shifting the graph of
   $y = x^2$ two units up and then one unit to the right.

▶ *Try It 1!*   Sketch the graph of $y = (x - 2)^2 + 3$.

Example 2   Sketch the graph of $y = -x^2 - 4x - 5$.

Solution   First, we rewrite the equation of the graph in the form

$y = -(x - h)^2 + k$ by completing the square.
$\begin{aligned}
y &= -x^2 - 4x - 5 \\
&= -(x^2 + 4x) - 5 \qquad \text{Make the coefficient of } x^2 \text{ to be 1.} \\
&= -\left[x^2 + 4x + \left(\frac{4}{2}\right)^2 - \left(\frac{4}{2}\right)^2\right] - 5 \\
&= -(x^2 + 4x + 4) + 4 - 5 \\
&= -(x + 2)^2 - 1
\end{aligned}$

$\therefore$ the maximum point is (−2, −1).
The line of symmetry is the line $x = -2$.

When $x = 0$, $\begin{aligned} y &= -(0 + 2)^2 - 1 \\ &= -5 \end{aligned}$

$\therefore$ the graph cuts the y-axis at (0, −5).

*Test your skill at matching
a function to its
corresponding graph at
http://www.univie.ac.at/
future.media/moe/tests/
fun1/erkennen.html.*

The diagram below shows the graph of $y = -x^2 - 4x - 5$.

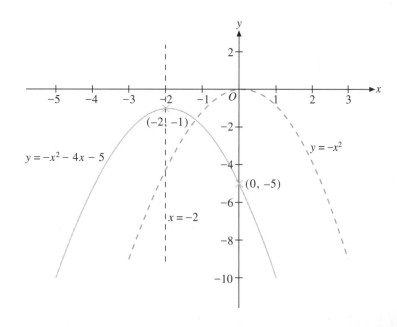

Note: The graph of $y = -(x + 2)^2 - 1$ may be obtained by shifting the graph of $y = -x^2$ one unit down and then two units to the left.

▶ *Try It 2!*　　Sketch the graph of $y = -x^2 + 6x - 11$.

B.　Graph of $y = \pm (x - p)(x - q)$

Consider the quadratic function $y = (x - p)(x - q)$, where p and q are constants.

When $y = 0$, 　　　　　$(x - p)(x - q) = 0$

$$x - p = 0 \quad \text{or} \quad x - q = 0$$
$$\therefore \qquad x = p \quad \text{or} \qquad x = q$$

$\therefore$ $x = p$ and $x = q$ are the roots of the equation $(x - p)(x - q) = 0$. The x-intercepts of the graph of $y = (x - p)(x - q)$ are at $x = p$ and $x = q$.

When $x = 0$, 　　　　　$y = (0 - p)(0 - q)$
$$= pq$$

$\therefore$ the graph cuts the y-axis at $(0, pq)$.

Figure 1 shows the sketch of the graph of $y = (x - p)(x - q)$, where p and q are positive.

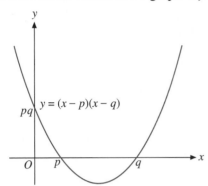

Figure 1

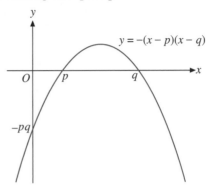

Figure 2

Similarly, we can sketch the graph of $y = -(x - p)(x - q)$ as shown in Figure 2. This graph also cuts the x-axis at $x = p$ and $x = q$, but it cuts the y-axis at $y = -pq$.

Note: When $p = q$, the function becomes
$$y = (x - p)^2 \quad \text{or} \quad y = -(x - p)^2.$$
The graph of this function touches the x-axis and has the turning point at $(p, 0)$. The line of symmetry of the graph is, therefore, $x = p$.

Example 3   Sketch the graph of $y = (x + 1)(x - 4)$. Find the minimum or maximum point of the function.

Solution
$$\begin{aligned} y &= (x + 1)(x - 4) \\ &= [x - (-1)](x - 4) \end{aligned}$$
$\therefore$ the x-intercepts are -1 and 4.

When $x = 0$, $\quad y = (0 + 1)(0 - 4) = -4$
$\therefore$ the y-intercept is -4.

Using the above information, we can sketch the graph of $y = (x + 1)(x - 4)$ as shown below.

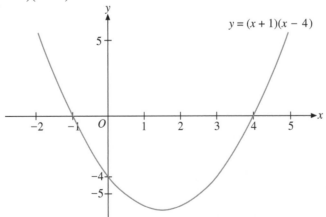

By symmetry, the minimum point is at $x = 1.5$.
When $x = 1.5$, $\quad y = (1.5 + 1)(1.5 - 4) = -6.25$
i.e. the minimum point is $(1.5, -6.25)$.

Alternatively, the x-intercepts can be obtained as follows:
When y = 0,
$(x + 1)(x - 4) = 0$
$\therefore$ x = -1 or x = 4.

Remark

By symmetry, (3, -4) is also a point on the graph of $y = (x + 1)(x - 4)$.

Remark

▶ *Try It 3!*   Sketch the graph of $y = (x + 2)(x - 1)$. Find the minimum or maximum point of the function.

Example 4   The daily profit y (in dollars) from the sales of a certain product can be represented by the function $y = 80x - x^2$, where x is the number of products produced in a day.
(a) Sketch the graph of $y = 80x - x^2$ for $x \geqslant 0$.
(b) How many products must be produced daily in order to maximise the profit? What is the maximum daily profit?

Solution   (a) First, we factorise $y = 80x - x^2$.

$$y = 80x - x^2$$
$$= -(x^2 - 80x)$$
$$= -x(x - 80)$$

∴ the x-intercepts are 0 and 80.

The diagram below shows the graph of $y = 80x - x^2$ for $x \geqslant 0$.

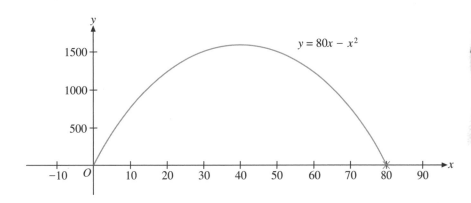

Discuss

Why do we draw the graph of $y = 80x - x^2$ for $x \geqslant 0$ only and not for all values of x?

(b) By symmetry, the maximum point is at $x = 40$.

When $x = 40$, $y = -40(40 - 80) = 1600$
i.e. the maximum point is (40, 1600).

∴ 40 products must be produced daily in order to maximise the profit.
The maximum daily profit is $1600.

▶ *Try It 4!*   Suppose the weekly profit y (in dollars) for producing and selling x vases is given by $y = 60x - x^2$.
(a) Sketch the graph of $y = 60x - x^2$ for $x \geqslant 0$.
(b) How many vases must be produced and sold in order to maximise the weekly profit? What is the maximum weekly profit?

Exercise 5.1

Basic Practice

1. State the turning point and sketch the graph of each of the following functions.
   (a) $y = x^2 + 2$
   (b) $y = (x + 1)^2$
   (c) $y = (x - 3)^2 + 4$
   (d) $y = (x + 2)^2 - 5$

2. State the line of symmetry and sketch the graph of each of the following functions.
   (a) $y = -x^2 - 3$
   (b) $y = -(x - 4)^2$
   (c) $y = -(x + 1)^2 - 2$
   (d) $y = -(x - 2)^2 + 3$

3. State the x-intercepts, the y-intercept and sketch the graph of each of the following functions.
   (a) $y = (x - 1)(x - 4)$
   (b) $y = (x + 3)(x - 1)$
   (c) $y = -(x + 2)(x + 3)$
   (d) $y = -x(x + 5)$

Further Practice

4. For each of the following,
   (i) express the function in the form $y = (x - h)^2 + k$ or $y = -(x - h)^2 + k$,
   (ii) state the maximum or minimum point of the function,
   (iii) sketch the graph of the function.

   (a) $y = x^2 + 2x + 3$
   (b) $y = -x^2 + 8x - 5$
   (c) $y = 5x - x^2$
   (d) $y = x^2 - 7x + 6$

5. For each of the following,
   (i) express the function in the form $y = (x - p)(x - q)$ or $y = -(x - p)(x - q)$,
   (ii) sketch the graph of the function,
   (iii) find the maximum or minimum point of the function.

   (a) $y = x^2 + 3x - 4$
   (b) $y = -x^2 + 3x - 2$
   (c) $y = -x^2 - 2x - 1$
   (d) $y = x^2 - 4$

Maths@Work

6. The difference between two numbers is 7. Suppose the smaller number is x and the product of the two numbers is y.
   (a) Express the other number in terms of x.
   (b) Express y in terms of x.
   (c) Sketch the graph of y against x.
   (d) Hence find the minimum value of the product of the two numbers. What are these two numbers?

7. The revenue y (in dollars) for selling x items is given by

$$y = 40x - x^2.$$

    (a) Sketch the graph of $y = 40x - x^2$ for $x \geqslant 0$.
    (b) How many items should be sold in order to have the maximum revenue? What is the maximum revenue?

Brainworks

8. (a) Find three quadratic functions such that the graph of each function has the turning point at $(3, -1)$.
    (b) Sketch the graphs of the functions that you have found in **(a)** on the same coordinate plane.

9. A ball is thrown and it flies in a trajectory, which can be represented by a quadratic function, across a field. The ball reaches its highest point of 5 m above a point 20 m away from where it is thrown.
    (a) How far away will the ball land from where it is thrown?
    (b) What is the quadratic equation for the ball's flight? Express it in the form $y = a(x - p)(x - q)$ where a, p and q are constants.
    (c) Sketch the path of the ball.
       (Assume that the ball starts at the point $(0, 0)$.)

5.2 Graphs Of Power Functions

The function $y = ax^n$, where **a** is a real constant and n is a rational number, is called a **power function**. We shall study the graph of this function for $n = -2, -1, 0, 1, 2$ and 3, in this section.

A. Graph of $y = ax^n$ for $n = 0, 1, 2,$ and 3

Case $n = 0$

When $n = 0$, $y = ax^n = ax^0$.
Since $x^0 = 1$ for all x except $x = 0$, we shall regard the function as

$$y = a.$$

This is the **constant function** that we learnt in Secondary Two. The diagram on the right shows the graph of two constant functions, $y = 3$ (i.e. $a = 3$) and $y = -2$ (i.e. $a = -2$).

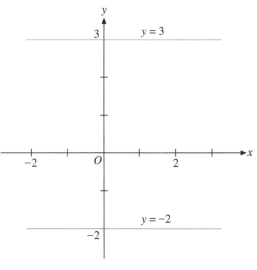

Case $n = 1$

When $n = 1$, the function $y = ax^n$ becomes
$$y = ax.$$

We learnt that this is a linear function. The diagram on the right shows the graphs of $y = 2x$ and $y = -x$.

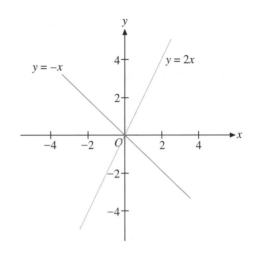

Case $n = 2$

When $n = 2$, $y = ax^n$ becomes
$$y = ax^2.$$

We know that this is a quadratic function. The diagram on the right shows the graphs of $y = x^2$ and $y = -\dfrac{1}{2}x^2$.

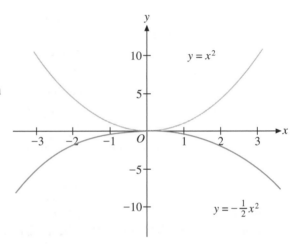

Case $n = 3$

When $n = 3$, $y = ax^n$ becomes
$$y = ax^3.$$

This function is new to us. It is known as a **cubic function**. Let us draw the graph of this function by plotting some points as shown in the following example.

Example 5   Draw the graph of the function $y = x^3$ for $-3 \leqslant x \leqslant 3$.

Solution   First, we set up a table of values for the function $y = x^3$.

x	-3	-2	-1	0	1	2	3
y	-27	-8	-1	0	1	8	27

Then, we plot the points and join them with a smooth curve to obtain the graph of the function.

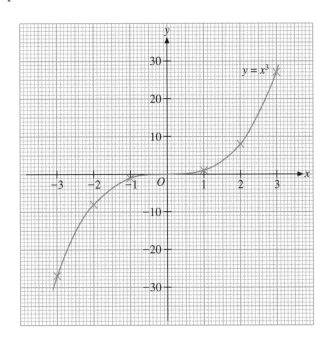

▶ *Try It 5!* Draw the graph of $y = -x^3$ for $-3 \leqslant x \leqslant 3$.

B. Graph of $y = ax^n$ for $n = -2$ and -1

When $n = -2$ and -1, $y = ax^n$ becomes $y = ax^{-2} = \dfrac{a}{x^2}$ and $y = ax^{-1} = \dfrac{a}{x}$, respectively.

As division by zero is meaningless, the functions $y = \dfrac{a}{x^2}$ and $y = \dfrac{a}{x}$ are undefined for $x = 0$. How do the graphs of these functions appear when x is very close to 0? Let us look at the following example.

Example 6 Draw the graph of $y = \dfrac{10}{x}$ for $-5 \leqslant x \leqslant 5$.

Solution $y = \dfrac{10}{x}$

x	−5	−4	−2	−1	−0.5	0.5	1	2	4	5
y	−2	−2.5	−5	−10	−20	20	10	5	2.5	2

The diagram below shows the graph of $y = \dfrac{10}{x}$.

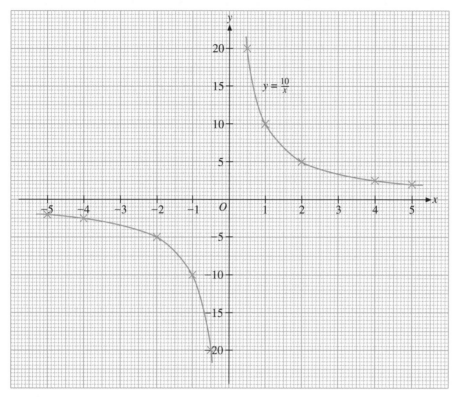

Discuss

What observations can you make about the graph for values of x towards the extreme left, the extreme right, and close to O?

Let us look at some extreme coordinates.

x	0.1	0.01	0.001	-100	-1000	-10^5
$y = \dfrac{10}{x}$	100	1000	10 000	-0.1	-0.01	-10^{-4}

What are the values of y when x = -0.1, -0.01, -0.001, 100, 1000 and 10^5?

Note: Note that the graph does not touch either the y-axis or the x-axis. Though the function is undefined at $x = 0$, when the numerical value of x is small enough, we can find a point on the graph as close as possible to the y-axis but does not touch it. On the other hand, when the numerical value of x is very large, the point on the graph becomes very close to the x-axis but does not touch it.

▶ *Try It 6!*   Draw the graph of $y = -\dfrac{12}{x}$ for $-5 \leqslant x \leqslant 5$.

Example 7   Draw the graph of $y = \dfrac{4}{x^2}$ for $-5 \leqslant x \leqslant 5$.

Solution $y = \dfrac{4}{x^2}$

x	–5	–4	–2	–1	–0.5	0.5	1	2	4	5
y	0.16	0.25	1	4	16	16	4	1	0.25	0.16

The diagram below shows the graph of $y = \dfrac{4}{x^2}$.

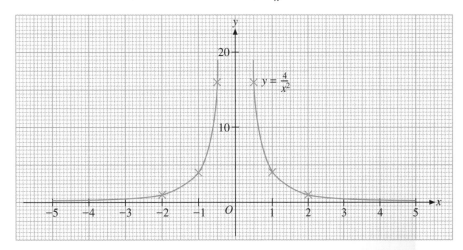

▶ *Try It 7!*   Draw the graph of $y = -\dfrac{5}{x^2}$ for $-5 \leqslant x \leqslant 5$.

Exercise 5.2

Basic Practice

1. Draw the graphs of the following functions for $-3 \leqslant x \leqslant 3$.

(a) $y = 2x^0$

(b) $y = -\dfrac{3}{2}x^0$

(c) $y = -2x$

(d) $y = \dfrac{3}{4}x$

(e) $y = \dfrac{1}{2}x^2$

(f) $y = -3x^2$

(g) $y = -\dfrac{1}{2}x^3$

(h) $y = 2x^3$

2. Draw the graphs of the following functions for $-4 \leqslant x \leqslant 4$.

   (a) $y = \dfrac{6}{x}$ (b) $y = -\dfrac{8}{x}$

   (c) $y = \dfrac{1}{x^2}$ (d) $y = -\dfrac{10}{x^2}$

Further Practice

3. The graph of the function $y = ax$ passes through the point $(6, 4)$.
   (a) Find the value of the constant a.
   (b) Sketch the graph of the function for $-2 \leqslant x \leqslant 6$.
   (c) Find the gradient of the graph.

   $\left(\text{Hint: Gradient of a line} = \dfrac{\text{rise}}{\text{run}}. \right)$

4. Sketch the graph of $y = x^2$ for $-4 \leqslant x \leqslant 4$.

5. The graph of the function $y = kx^3$ passes through the point $(-2, 16)$.
   (a) Find the value of the constant k.
   (b) Draw the graph of the function for $-2 \leqslant x \leqslant 2$.

6. (a) Draw the graphs of the functions $y = x$ and $y = \dfrac{1}{x}$ on the same diagram for $-5 \leqslant x \leqslant 5$.
   (b) State the coordinates of the intersecting points of the two graphs.
   (c) Describe the shape of the graph of $y = \dfrac{1}{x}$ with respect to the line $y = x$.

Maths@Work

7. The area of a rectangular poster is 4 m^2. The dimensions of the poster are x m by y m.
   (a) Express y as a function of x.
   (b) Copy and complete the following table of corresponding values of x and y.

x	0.25	0.5	1	2	4	5
y						

   (c) Draw the graph of the function for $0 < x \leqslant 5$.

8. The force of attraction, F, between two pieces of magnets is given by the function

$$F = \frac{100}{d^2}$$

where d is the distance between the magnets, and F and d are in appropriate units.

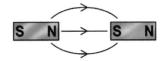

   (a) Draw the graph of the function for $0 < d \le 10$.
   (b) Find the percentage change in F when d increases from 5 units to 10 units.
   (c) Describe the change in F when the value of d approaches zero.

Brainworks

9. Are the functions $y = \frac{2x}{x}$ and $y = 2$ equivalent? Explain briefly, with diagrams if necessary.

5.3 Graphs Of Sums Of Power Functions

When two power functions are added together, they form a new function. For example, the sum of $y = x$ and $y = \frac{1}{x}$ is

$$y = x + \frac{1}{x}.$$

The shape of the graph of the new function may be quite different from those of the individual functions. We can use the plotting-point method to draw the new function.

Example 8   (a) Draw the graph of the function $y = x^3 - x^2 - 2x$ for $-2 \le x \le 3$.
                (b) Use your graph to solve the equation $x^3 - x^2 - 2x = 5$.

Solution   (a) $y = x^3 - x^2 - 2x$

x	-2	-1	0	1	2	3
y	-8	0	0	-2	0	12

The diagram below shows the graph of $y = x^3 - x^2 - 2x$.

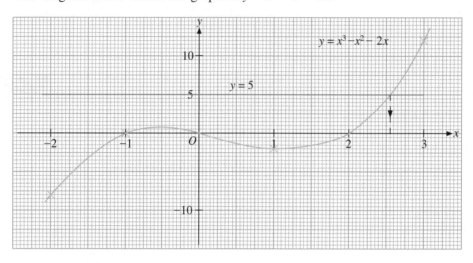

(b) Add the line $y = 5$ to the diagram in (a). The x-coordinate of the point of intersection of the line and the graph of $y = x^3 - x^2 - 2x$ gives the solution to the equation $x^3 - x^2 - 2x = 5$.
∴ the required solution is $x = 2.55$.

Note: • When all the terms in a function are positive powers of x or constants, the graph is a smooth and continuous curve.

• When we are in doubt how a graph should be drawn for a certain range of values of x, we should plot additional point(s) for that range. In this example, we should plot the point $(-0.5, 0.625)$.

▶ **Try It 8!** (a) Draw the graph of the function $y = x^3 - 4x$ for $-3 \leqslant x \leqslant 3$.
(b) Use your graph to solve the equation $x^3 - 4x = 10$, giving your answer correct to 1 decimal place.

Example 9 (a) Draw the graph of the function $y = x + \dfrac{1}{x}$ for $-3 \leqslant x \leqslant 3$.
(b) Find the maximum and minimum points of the graph.

Solution (a) Since the function $y = x + \dfrac{1}{x}$ consists of the term $\dfrac{1}{x}$, it is undefined at $x = 0$.

$y = x + \dfrac{1}{x}$

x	-3	-2	-1	-0.5	0.5	1	2	3
y	-3.33	-2.5	-2	-2.5	2.5	2	2.5	3.33

The diagram below shows the graph of $y = x + \dfrac{1}{x}$.

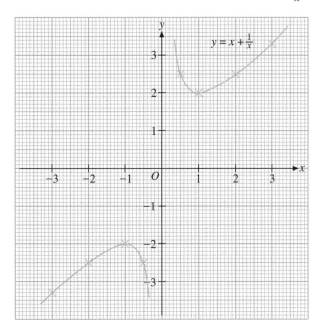

(b) $(-1, -2)$ is the maximum point of the graph.

$(1, 2)$ is the minimum point of the graph.

Note: The point $(1, 2)$ is a minimum point of the graph. This means the minimum value of the sum of a positive number x and its reciprocal $\dfrac{1}{x}$ is 2 when $x = 1$.

▶ *Try It 9!* (a) Draw the graph of the function $y = x + \dfrac{1}{x^2}$ for $-3 \leqslant x \leqslant 3$.

(b) Find the minimum point of the graph.

Exercise 5.3

Basic Practice

1. Draw the graphs of the following functions for $-3 \leqslant x \leqslant 3$.

(a) $y = x + 2$

(b) $y = x^2 - 4$

(c) $y = x^3 + 5$

(d) $y = 3 - \dfrac{1}{x}$

2. Draw the graphs of the following functions for $-3 \leqslant x \leqslant 3$.

   (a) $y = 2x - x^2$

   (b) $y = x^3 + x$

   (c) $y = 4x - x^3$

   (d) $y = x^2 + \dfrac{1}{x^2}$

Further Practice

3. **(a)** Draw the graph of $y = 2x^3 - x + 2$ for $-2 \leqslant x \leqslant 2$.

   (b) Use your graph to solve the equation $2x^3 - x + 2 = 3$.

4. **(a)** Draw the graph of $y = -x^3 + 3x + 2$ for $-2 \leqslant x \leqslant 3$.

   (b) Find the maximum and minimum points of the graph.

5. **(a)** Draw the graph of $y = x^3 + 4x^2 + 4x$ for $-3 \leqslant x \leqslant 1$.

   (b) Use your graph to solve the equation $x^3 + 4x^2 + 4x = -1$.

6. **(a)** Draw the graph of $y = x^3 - 2x - \dfrac{1}{x^2}$ for $-2 \leqslant x \leqslant 2$.

   (b) Find the maximum point of the graph.

   (c) Use your graph to solve the equation $x^3 - 2x - \dfrac{1}{x^2} = x$.

7. **(a)** Draw the graph of $y = x + 3 - \dfrac{1}{x}$ for $-5 \leqslant x \leqslant 4$.

   (b) Use your graph to solve the equation $x + 1 - \dfrac{1}{x} = 0$.

Maths@Work

8. The function

$$y = -0.2t^3 + 5t \quad \text{for } 0 \leqslant t \leqslant 5$$

gives the approximate concentration y (in a certain unit) of a drug in a person's blood t hours after taking a pill containing the drug.

   (a) Draw the graph of $y = -0.2t^3 + 5t$ for $0 \leqslant t \leqslant 5$.

   (b) Estimate from the graph,

   (i) the maximum concentration and the corresponding time,

   (ii) the times at which the concentration is 6 units.

9. **(a)** Draw the graph of the function $y = 4 - \dfrac{1}{x^2}$ for $-3 \leqslant x \leqslant 3$.

   (b) The cross-section of a bench is in the shape bounded by the graph of $y = 4 - \dfrac{1}{x^2}$, the x- and y-axes, and the lines $x = 3$ and $y = 4$. Make a sketch of the cross-section.

Brainworks

10. The diagram shows the graph of a function $y = ax^3 + bx^2 + cx$, where a, b and c are constants. Find the equation of a function such that its graph has a shape similar to that shown in the diagram.

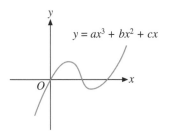

5.4 Graphs Of Exponential Functions

In the quadratic function $y = x^2$, the variable x is the base of a power. It is different from the function $y = 2^x$ in which the variable x is the index. The function $y = 2^x$ is called an **exponential function**. In general, an exponential function is defined as follows:

> If $a > 0$ and $a \neq 1$, and k is a constant, then
>
> $$y = ka^x$$
>
> is called an exponential function with base a.

Note that if $a = 1$, the function becomes the constant function $y = k$. This is not an exponential function.

Exponential functions can be used to describe certain growth and decay phenomena in biology, chemistry, physics and economics. It is an important function in advanced mathematics. We shall confine our discussion on this group of functions for those cases where the base a is a positive integer.

Example 10 Draw the graph of $y = 3^x$ for $-3 \leqslant x \leqslant 3$.

Solution First, we set up a table of values of x and y.

$y = 3^x$

x	-3	-2	-1	0	1	2	3
y	$\dfrac{1}{27}$	$\dfrac{1}{9}$	$\dfrac{1}{3}$	1	3	9	27

Then we plot the points and join them with a smooth curve to obtain the graph of $y = 3^x$ as shown below.

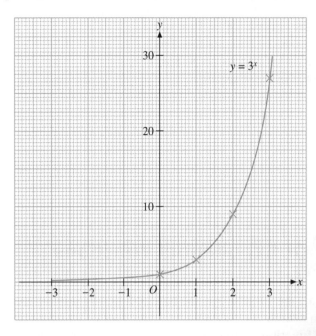

▶ Try It 10! Draw the graph of $y = 2^x$ for $-3 \leqslant x \leqslant 3$.

Example 11 The number of bacteria in a culture is given by the function

$$y = 50(2^t)$$

where t is the number of hours after the start of the observation.
(a) Find the number of bacteria in the culture
  (i) at the start of the observation,
  (ii) 3 hours later.
(b) Draw the graph of $y = 50(2^t)$ for $0 \leqslant t \leqslant 4$.
(c) Estimate the time at which the number of bacteria is 300.

culture

Solution **(a) (i)** $y = 50(2^t)$

At the start, $t = 0$. Putting $t = 0$ into the function,

$y = 50(2^0)$
$\quad = 50 \times 1$
$\quad = 50$
i.e. the number of bacteria at the start is 50.

(ii) When $t = 3$,
$y = 50(2^3)$
$\quad = 400$
i.e. the number of bacteria 3 hours later is 400.

$a^0 = 1$ if $a \neq 0$.

Recall

(b) $y = 50(2^t)$

t	0	1	2	3	4
y	50	100	200	400	800

The diagram below shows the graph of $y = 50(2^t)$.

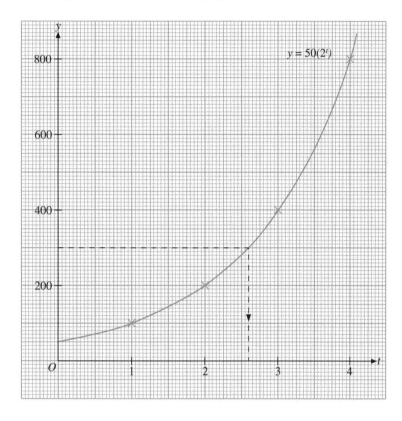

(c) Draw the horizontal line, $y = 300$, to meet the graph. Drop a perpendicular line to the t-axis from the point of intersection to read the corresponding time.

∴ the required time is 2.6 hours.

▷ *Try It 11!* The number of yeast cells in a cup of water at time t hours after the first observation is given by

$$y = 60(2^t).$$

(a) Find the number of yeast cells in the cup
  (i) when first observed,
  (ii) 2 hours later.
(b) Draw the graph of $y = 60(2^t)$ for $0 \leqslant t \leqslant 4$.
(c) Estimate the time at which the number of yeast cells is 400.

Exercise 5.4

Basic Practice

1. (a) Copy and complete the following table for $y = 5^x$.

x	-2	-1	0	1	2	3
y						

   (b) Draw the graph of $y = 5^x$ for $-2 \leqslant x \leqslant 3$.

2. (a) Copy and complete the following table for $y = -2^x$.

x	-2	-1	0	1	2	3
y						

   (b) Draw the graph of $y = -2^x$ for $-2 \leqslant x \leqslant 3$.

Further Practice

3. (a) Draw the graph of $y = 2(3^x)$ for $-2 \leqslant x \leqslant 2$.
   (b) Use your graph to find the value of x when $2(3^x) = 10$.

4. (a) Draw the graph of $y = -5(4^x)$ for $-2 \leqslant x \leqslant 2$.
   (b) Use your graph to find the value of x when $-5(4^x) = -60$.

5. (a) Draw the graph of $y = 10^x$ for $-1 \leqslant x \leqslant 1$.
   (b) If $10^x = 8$, find the value of x from the graph.

Maths@Work

6. The asset y (in thousand dollars) of a company after t years in business is given by the function $y = 50(3^t)$ for $0 \leqslant t \leqslant 3$.
   (a) Find the asset of the company
       (i) initially,
       (ii) after 3 years in business.
   (b) Draw the graph of $y = 50(3^t)$ for $0 \leqslant t \leqslant 3$.
   (c) Estimate from the graph the time at which the asset would just reach $1 million.

7. **(a)** Draw the graphs of the exponential function $y = 2^x$ and the quadratic function $y = x^2$ on the same diagram for $-1 \leqslant x \leqslant 5$.

   (b) Find the points of intersection of the two graphs, correct to 1 decimal place.

   (c) Use the graphs to solve the equation $2^x = x^2$.

   (d) Compare the shapes of the two graphs.

8. **(a)** Draw the graphs of the exponential functions $y = 2^x$, $y = 3^x$ and $y = 4^x$ on the same diagram for $-2 \leqslant x \leqslant 3$ using Sketchpad or graph paper.

   (b) Describe some common properties of the graphs.

5.5 Gradients Of Curves

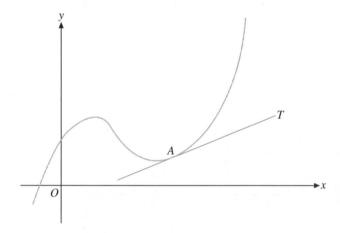

In the above figure, A is a point on the curve. The line AT which touches the curve at A is said to be a **tangent** to the curve at A.

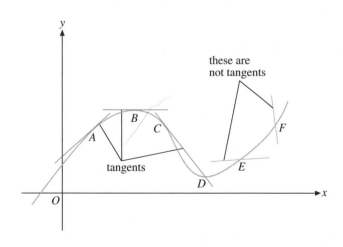

In the above figure, the lines at *A*, *B* and *C* are tangents to the curve at the respective points, while the lines at *E* and *F* are not tangents at those points. Note that a tangent to a curve may cut the curve at more than one point. For example, the tangent at *C* cuts the curve again at *D*.

The **gradient of a curve** at a point on it is defined to be the gradient of the tangent at that point. Along a curve, its gradient may vary from positive, zero to negative. Let us look at some examples.

Example 12 (a) Draw the graph of $y = 4 - x^2$ for $-3 \leqslant x \leqslant 3$.
  (b) Find the gradient of the graph at the point where
   (i) $x = -2$,
   (ii) $x = 0$,
   (iii) $x = 1$.

Solution (a) $y = 4 - x^2$

x	-3	-2	-1	0	1	2	3
y	-5	0	3	4	3	0	-5

The diagram below shows the graph of $y = 4 - x^2$.

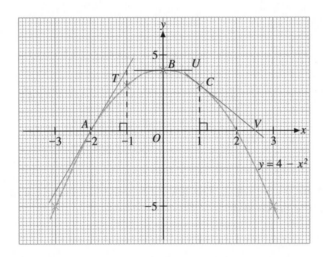

(b) (i) Draw the tangent *AT* to the curve at $A(-2, 0)$.

  Gradient of the curve at *A* = gradient of the line *AT*

$$= \frac{\text{rise}}{\text{run}}$$

$$= \frac{4}{1}$$

$$= 4$$

(ii) Draw the tangent BU to the curve at $B(0, 4)$.
As BU is a horizontal line,

gradient of the curve at B = gradient of the line BU
$$= 0$$

(iii) Draw the tangent CV to the curve at $C(1, 3)$.

Gradient of the curve at C = gradient of the line CV
$$= \frac{-3}{1.5}$$
$$= -2$$

Note: The gradient of the tangent to the graph of $y = 4 - x^2$ is positive for $x < 0$, zero for $x = 0$, and negative for $x > 0$.

▶ *Try It 12!* **(a)** Draw the graph of $y = x^2 - 1$ for $-3 \leqslant x \leqslant 3$.
(b) Find the gradient of the graph at the point where
  (i) $x = -1$,
  (ii) $x = 0$,
  (iii) $x = 2$.

Example 13 A manufacturer wants to make a closed cylindrical can of capacity 400 cm^3. Suppose the base radius of the can is x cm and the height of the can is h cm.
(a) (i) Express h in terms of x.
  (ii) Let $S \text{ cm}^2$ be the total surface area of the can. Take $\pi = 3$.

Show that $S = 6x^2 + \dfrac{800}{x}$.

(b) Draw the graph of $S = 6x^2 + \dfrac{800}{x}$ for $2 \leqslant x \leqslant 8$.

(c) Use your graph to find
  (i) the values of x for which the total surface area is 350 cm^2,
  (ii) the gradient of the curve at $x = 5$,
  (iii) the dimensions of the can which has the least possible total surface area.

Solution **(a) (i)** Capacity $= \pi x^2 h$
$$400 = \pi x^2 h$$

$$\therefore \quad h = \frac{400}{\pi x^2}$$

(ii) $S = 2 \times$ base area + curved surface area
$$= 2\pi x^2 + 2\pi xh$$

$$= 2\pi x^2 + 2\pi x\left(\frac{400}{\pi x^2}\right)$$

$$= 2(3)x^2 + \frac{800}{x} \qquad \text{Take } \pi = 3.$$

$$\therefore \ S = 6x^2 + \frac{800}{x}$$

(b) $S = 6x^2 + \dfrac{800}{x}$

x	2	3	4	5	6	7	8
y	424	320.7	296	310	349.3	408.3	484

The figure below shows the graph of $S = 6x^2 + \dfrac{800}{x}$.

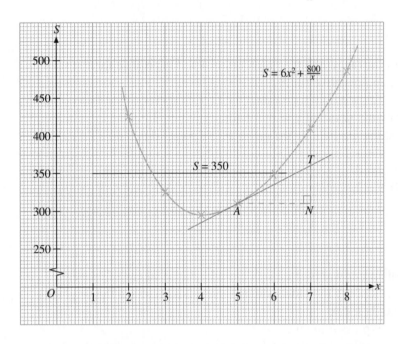

(c) (i) We add the line $S = 350$ to the graph in **(b)**.
The required values of x are 2.6 and 6.0.

(ii) Draw the tangent to the curve at $A(5, 310)$.

$$\text{Gradient of the curve at } A = \frac{TN}{AN}$$

$$= \frac{50}{2}$$

$$= 25$$

(iii) From the graph, $(4, 296)$ is a minimum point.
When $x = 4$,

$$h = \frac{400}{3 \times 4^2}$$

$$= 8.3 \quad \text{(correct to 1 d.p.).}$$

∴ the required dimensions are base radius = 4 cm and
height = 8.3 cm.

Note: • We have to use appropriate scales for a graph. In this example, the vertical scale starts from 250.

• There is a limitation in the accuracy when finding the gradient of a curve by the graphical method of drawing a tangent.

▶ *Try It 13!* An open rectangular box has a square base of side x cm and height h cm. The volume of the box is 100 cm^3.

(a) (i) Express h in terms of x.

(ii) Let A cm^2 be the total external surface area of the box. Show that $A = x^2 + \dfrac{400}{x}$.

(b) Draw the graph of $A = x^2 + \dfrac{400}{x}$ for $3 \leqslant x \leqslant 10$.

(c) Use your graph to find

(i) the values of x for which the total external surface area is 120 cm^2,

(ii) the gradient of the curve at $x = 4$,

(iii) the dimensions of the box which has the least possible total external surface area.

Exercise 5.5

Basic Practice

1. Find the gradient of each of the following curves at the point A.

(a)
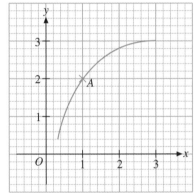

(b)
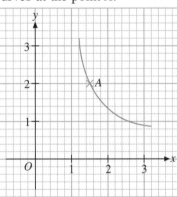

(c)
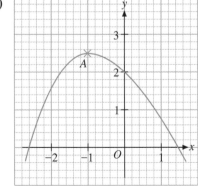

(d)
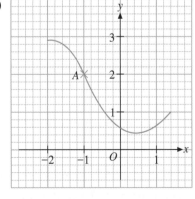

2. **(a)** Draw the graph of $y = 2x^2 + 1$ for $-3 \leqslant x \leqslant 3$.
    (b) By drawing a tangent, find the gradient of the curve at the point
        (i) $A(0, 1)$,
        (ii) $B(2, 9)$.

3. **(a)** Draw the graph of $y = x^3$ for $-2 \leqslant x \leqslant 2$.
    (b) By drawing a tangent, find the gradient of the curve at the point where
        (i) $x = 0$
        (ii) $x = -1$.

4. **(a)** Draw the graph of $y = \dfrac{2}{x}$ for $\dfrac{1}{2} \leqslant x \leqslant 4$.

    (b) By drawing a tangent, find the gradient of the curve at the point $A(2, 1)$.

Further Practice

5. **(a)** Sketch the graph of $y = x^2 + x$ for $-3 \leqslant x \leqslant 2$.
    (b) Find the minimum point of the graph.
    (c) Find the gradient of the graph at the minimum point.

6. **(a)** Draw the graph of the curve $y = 1 - x^3$ for $-2.5 \leqslant x \leqslant 2.5$.
    (b) By drawing a tangent, find the gradient of the curve at the point
        (i) $A(0, 1)$,
        (ii) $B(-1, 2)$.
    (c) The tangent to the curve at B meets the curve at another point. Find the coordinates of that point.

7. **(a)** Draw the graph of the curve $y = x^2 + \dfrac{1}{x^2}$ for $\dfrac{1}{2} \leqslant x \leqslant 3$.

    (b) Find the minimum point of the curve.
    (c) Find the gradient of the curve at
        (i) the minimum point,
        (ii) the point where $x = 2$.

    (d) Use your graph to solve the equation $x^2 + \dfrac{1}{x^2} = 3$.

8. **(a)** Draw the graph of the curve $y = x(9 - x^2)$ for $-3.5 \leqslant x \leqslant 3.5$.
    (b) Find the maximum and minimum points on the curve.
    (c) Find the gradient of the curve at the point where $x = 2.5$ by drawing a tangent.
    (d) Write down the interval of values of x for which the gradient of the curve is positive.
    (e) **(i)** Draw the line $y = \dfrac{5}{2}x$ on the diagram in **(a)**.
        (ii) Hence use your graph to solve the equation $2x(9 - x^2) = 5x$.

Maths@Work

9. When x printers are sold, the profit y made by a computer retailer is given by the equation $y = k(x - 10)(90 - x)$, where k is a constant and $0 \leqslant x \leqslant 90$. It is known that the profit is $600 for 30 printers sold.
   (a) Find the value of k.
   (b) Draw the graph of $y = k(x - 10)(90 - x)$ for $0 \leqslant x \leqslant 90$.
   (c) By drawing a tangent, find the gradient of the graph at the point where $x = 30$.
   (d) (i) Find the number of printers that should be sold to get the maximum profit.
       (ii) Find the profit per printer using the result in (d)(i).
   (e) (i) Draw the line $y = 12x$ on the diagram in (b).
       (ii) Hence find the number of printers sold such that the profit per printer is $12.

10.

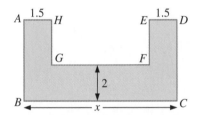

The diagram shows the cross-section $ABCDEFGH$ of a rectangular tray. BC is x cm wide, the side walls are 1.5 cm thick and the bottom is 2 cm thick. The area of the rectangle $ABCD$ is 50 cm². The rectangular hollow area $EFGH$ is y cm².
   (a) Express the lengths of the following in terms of x.
       (i) AB
       (ii) FG
       (iii) EF

   (b) Show that $y = 56 - 2x - \dfrac{150}{x}$.

   (c) The table below shows some corresponding values of x and y for the function $y = 56 - 2x - \dfrac{150}{x}$.

x	3	4	6	8	10	12
y	0	10.5	19	21.25	21	p

   (i) Find the value of p.
   (ii) Using a scale of 1 cm to 1 unit on the x-axis and 1 cm to 5 units on the y-axis, draw the graph of $y = 56 - 2x - \dfrac{150}{x}$ for $3 \leqslant x \leqslant 12$.

(d) From your graph, find

    (i) the smaller value of x such that $y = 20$,

    (ii) the gradient of the curve at the point $(4, 10.5)$,

    (iii) the value of x for which the area of *EFGH* is a maximum,

    (iv) the maximum area of *EFGH*.

Brainworks

11. Can a straight line be tangent to a curve at more than one point? Illustrate your answer with a diagram.

12. Sketch a curve in which the gradients of the curve at the points where $x = 0$, $x = 1$ and $x = 2$ are 2, 0 and -1 respectively.

In A Nutshell

1. Quadratic Graphs

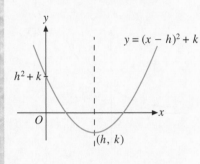

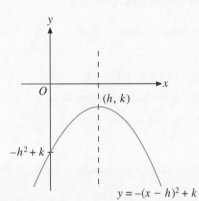

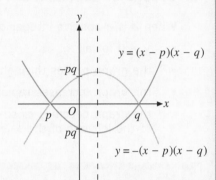

2. Graphs of Power Functions $y = ax^n$

(a) $n = -2$, $a = 1$

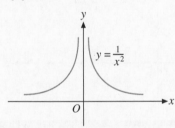

(b) $n = -1$, $a = 1$

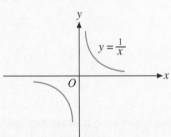

(c) $n = 0$, $a = 3$

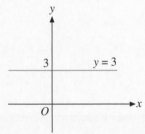

(d) $n = 1$, $a = -2$

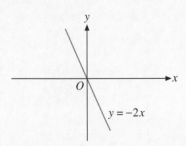

(e) $n = 2$, $a = -3$

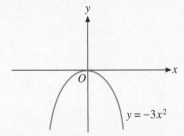

(f) $n = 3$, $a = 1$

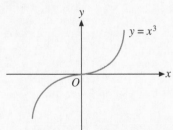

3. Graphs of Exponential Functions $y = ka^x$

When a is a positive integer greater than 1 and $k > 0$,

- $y > 0$ for all x,
- the graph passes through the point $(0, k)$,
- the graph increases rapidly for large values of x,
- the graph becomes close to the x-axis when x tends to the left end of the x-axis.

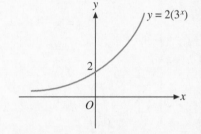

4. Gradients of Curves

Gradient of a curve at a point A

= gradient of the tangent to the curve at A

= $\dfrac{\text{rise}}{\text{run}}$

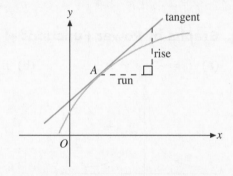

Revision Exercise 5

1. The diagram shows the graph of $y = x^2 + 4x$ which passes through the origin and a point A on the x-axis.

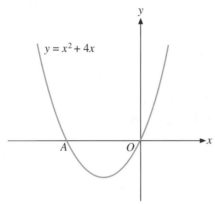

   (a) Find the coordinates of A.
   (b) State the equation of the line of symmetry of the graph.
   (c) Find the minimum point on the graph.
   (d) Find the interval of values of x at which the gradient of the graph is positive.

2. (a) Solve the equation $-x^2 + 4x - 3 = 0$.
   (b) Express $-x^2 + 4x - 3$ in the form $-(x - h)^2 + k$, where h and k are constants.
   (c) Hence sketch the graph of $y = -x^2 + 4x - 3$.
   (d) State the maximum point of the graph.
   (e) What is the gradient of the curve at the maximum point?

3. The table below shows some corresponding values of x and y, where $y = x(x + 2)(x - 3)$.

x	-2.5	-2	-1	0	1	2	3	4
y	p	0	4	0	-6	-8	0	24

   (a) Find the value of p.
   (b) Using a scale of 1 cm to 1 unit on the x-axis and 1 cm to 5 units on the y-axis, draw the graph of $y = x(x + 2)(x - 3)$ for $-2.5 \leqslant x \leqslant 4$.
   (c) From the graph, find
       (i) the minimum and maximum points of the graph,
       (ii) the gradient of the graph at the point $(3, 0)$.
   (d) (i) Draw the graph of $y = 2^x$ for $-2.5 \leqslant x \leqslant 4$ on the diagram in (b).
       (ii) Hence use your graph to solve the equation $x(x + 2)(x - 3) = 2^x$.

4. (a) Copy and complete the following table of corresponding values of x and y, where $y = x^2 + \dfrac{20}{x}$. Give your answers correct to 1 decimal place.

x	0.5	1	2	3	4	5	6	7
y								

(b) Taking 1 cm to represent 1 unit on the x-axis and 1 cm to represent 10 units on the y-axis, draw the graph of $y = x^2 + \dfrac{20}{x}$ for $0.5 \leqslant x \leqslant 7$.

(c) By drawing a tangent, find the gradient of the graph at $x = 1$.

(d) Use your graph to find the solutions of the equation

 (i) $x^2 + \dfrac{20}{x} = 30$,

 (ii) $x^2 + \dfrac{20}{x} = 10$.

(e) Use your graph to find the minimum value of $x^2 + \dfrac{20}{x}$ for $0.5 \leqslant x \leqslant 7$.

(f) (i) Draw the graph of the straight line $y = -8x + 40$ on the same axes.

 (ii) Write down, but do not simplify, an equation in x which has the x-coordinates of the intersecting points of the two graphs as solutions.

5. A piece of wire 72 cm long is cut into 12 pieces to form a cuboid frame of x cm by x cm by h cm as shown.

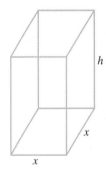

(a) Express h in terms of x.

(b) Let y cm^3 be the volume of the cuboid. Show that $y = 18x^2 - 2x^3$.

(c) Draw the graph of $y = 18x^2 - 2x^3$ for $0 \leqslant x \leqslant 9$.

(d) By drawing a tangent, find the gradient of the graph at $x = 7$.

(e) Use the graph to find the value(s) of x for which the volume of the cuboid is

 (i) 150 cm^3,

 (ii) maximum.

6. A cake has a square base of side x cm and a height of 8 cm. A layer of 100 cm^3 of icing is coated uniformly on the top of the cake. Suppose the finished cake with the icing is y cm high.

   (a) Show that $y = 8 + \dfrac{100}{x^2}$.

   (b) Using a scale of 1 cm to 1 unit on the x-axis and 1 cm to 5 units on the y-axis, draw the graph of $y = 8 + \dfrac{100}{x^2}$ for $2 \leqslant x \leqslant 10$.

   (c) By drawing a tangent, find the gradient of the curve at the point where $x = 5$.

7. **Answer the whole of this question on a sheet of graph paper.**
   The table below gives some values of x and the corresponding values of y, correct to two decimal places, where $y = x(1 + x)(4 - x)$.

x	-1	-0.5	0	0.5	1	1.5	2	2.5	3	3.5	4
y	0	-1.13	0	2.63	6	9.38	p	13.13	12	7.88	q

   (a) (i) Find the value of p and the value of q. [1]
       (ii) Using a scale of 2 cm to 1 unit, draw a horizontal x-axis for $-1 \leqslant x \leqslant 4$.
            Using a scale of 1 cm to 1 unit, draw a vertical y-axis for $-2 \leqslant y \leqslant 14$.
            On your axes, plot the points given in the table and join them with a smooth curve. [3]
       (iii) Using your graph, find the values of x for which $y = 3$. [2]

   (b) By drawing a tangent, find the gradient of the curve at the point where $x = 3$. [2]

   (c) On the axes used in part (a), draw the graph of $y = 10 - x$ for values of x in the range $-1 \leqslant x \leqslant 4$. [2]

   (d) Write down, and simplify, the cubic equation which is satisfied by the values of x at the points where the two graphs intersect. [2]

   NP2/2000/9

8. (a) The sketch represents the graph of $y = x^n$.
      Write down a possible value of n.

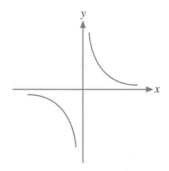

      [1]

(b) The point (1, 1) is marked on each diagram in the answer space. On these diagrams, sketch the graphs of

(i) $y = \dfrac{1}{3}x + 1$,

(ii) $y = \dfrac{1}{x^2}$,

(iii) $y = 2^x$.

Answer **(b)(i)**

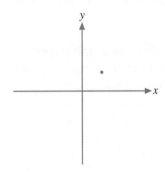

[1]

(ii)

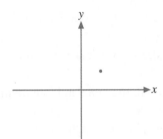

[1]

(iii)

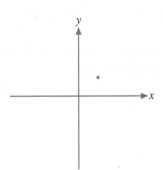

[1]

NP1/2002/17

9. A rectangular piece of card measures 20 cm by 14 cm.
Squares of side x cm are cut from the four corners and the card is folded to make an open box.

(a) Show that the volume, V cm^3, of the box is given by
$$V = 4x(10 - x)(7 - x).$$ [1]

(b) You are asked to find the value of x which will produce the greatest volume of the box.

You should use the table and the grid to help you in your investigation.

Marks will be awarded for clear working. [4]

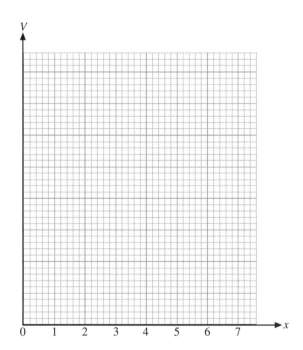

10. Answer the whole of this question on a sheet of graph paper.

A man stood at the top of a tower.

He threw a ball vertically upwards.

The height, h metres, of the ball **above the top of the tower** at a time t seconds after it was thrown is given by the formula $h = 22t - 4.9t^2$.

The table below shows some values of t and the corresponding values of h, correct to 1 decimal place.

t	0	1	2	2.5	3	4	5	6
h	0.0	17.1	24.4	24.4	21.9	9.6	−12.5	p

(a) Explain the significance of the value $h = -12.5$ when $t = 5$. [1]

(b) Find the value of p. [1]

(c) Using a scale of 2 cm to 1 second, draw a horizontal t-axis for $0 \leqslant t \leqslant 6$.

Using a scale of 2 cm to 10 metres, draw a vertical h-axis for $-50 \leqslant h \leqslant 30$.

On your axes, plot the points given in the table and join them with a smooth curve. [3]

(d) Use your graph to find

　(i)　the greatest height of the ball above the top of the tower, [1]

　(ii)　the length of time for which the ball was more than 20 metres above the top of the tower. [2]

(e) (i)　By drawing a tangent, find the gradient of the graph at (4, 9.6). [2]

　(ii)　Explain what your answer to **(e)(i)** tells you about the motion of the ball at $t = 4$. [1]

(f) The ball hit the ground 5.4 seconds after it was thrown. Use your graph to find the height of the tower. [1]

NP2/2002/10

11. Answer the whole of this question on a sheet of graph paper.

A solid cylinder of radius r centimetres and height h centimetres has a volume of 100π cm^3.

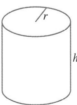

(a) (i)　Show that $h = \dfrac{100}{r^2}$. [1]

　(ii)　The cylinder has a total surface area of πy square centimetres.

　　Show that $y = 2r^2 + \dfrac{200}{r}$. [1]

(b) The table below shows some values of r and the corresponding values of y, correct to the nearest whole number.

r	1	1.5	2	3	4	5	6
y	202	138	108	85	82	90	p

    (i) Find the value of p.   [1]

    (ii) Using a scale of 2 cm to represent 1 cm, draw a horizontal r-axis for $1 \leqslant r \leqslant 6$.

       Using a scale of 2 cm to represent 20 cm^2, draw a vertical y-axis for $70 \leqslant y \leqslant 220$.

       On your axes, plot the points given in the table and join them with a smooth curve.   [3]

(c) Use your graph to find the values of r for which $y = 100$.   [2]

(d) By drawing a tangent, find the gradient of the graph at the point where $r = 2$.   [2]

(e) Use your graph to find

    (i) the value of r for which y is least,   [1]

    (ii) the smallest possible value of the total surface area of the cylinder.   [1]

NP2/2004/10

Extend Your Learning Curve

Maximising the Volume of a Box

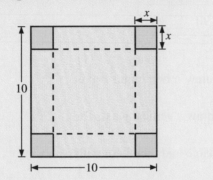
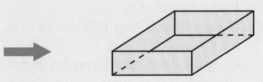

A square piece of paper is of side 10 cm. A small square of side x cm is cut from each of its four corners. The piece of paper is then folded into an open box. What is the maximum possible volume of the box that can be formed?

Write In Your Journal

In this chapter, two types of functions were introduced to you: power functions in the form $y = ax^n$ and exponential functions in the form $y = ka^x$. Write down briefly how you would revise what you have learnt about the graphs of these two types of functions.

6 Properties Of Circles

The design of alloy wheels for cars makes good use of the symmetry properties of circles. Apart from providing better motor performance, they also enhance the appearance of cars.

Let's learn to...

- understand the symmetry properties of circles
- understand the properties of chords of a circle
- understand the properties of angles in a circle
- state the properties of angles in opposite segments
- understand the properties of tangents to a circle
- solve problems involving properties of circles

6.1 Chords Of A Circle

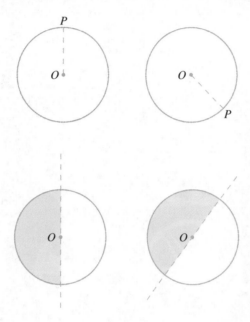

A circle is a beautiful and symmetrical shape. When a circle is rotated through any angle about its centre, its orientation remains the same. When any straight line is drawn through its centre, it divides the circle into two identical semicircles.

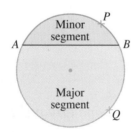

A diameter is the longest chord of a circle.

Remark

Many properties of a circles are based on its symmetry properties. Let us first study the properties of the chords of a circle. A **chord** of a circle is a line segment which has its two end points on the circumference of the circle. In the above circle, the line segment *AB* is a **chord** of the circle. The region bounded by the arc *APB* and *AB* is called a **minor segment** of the circle because it is smaller than a semicircle. The region bounded by the arc *AQB* and *AB* is called a **major segment** of the circle.

Note that arc *APB* is also called **minor arc** *AB* and arc *AQB* is called **major arc** *AB*.

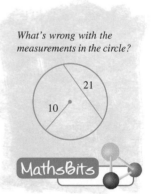
What's wrong with the measurements in the circle?

MathsBits

Class Activity 1

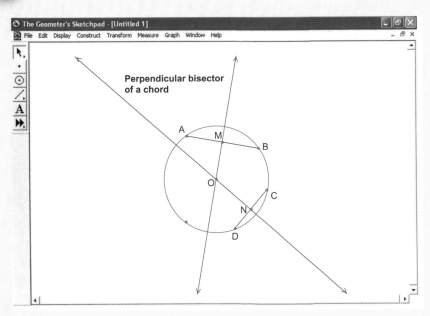

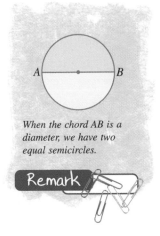

When the chord AB is a diameter, we have two equal semicircles.

Remark

Tasks

Do the following steps using Sketchpad.

(a) Construct a circle with centre O using the **Compass** tool.

(b) Draw two chords AB and CD on the circle using the **Line Segment** tool.

(c) Click the chord AB and then select the menu **Construct | Midpoint** to mark the midpoint M of AB.

(d) Click M and the chord AB, and then select the menu **Construct | Perpendicular Line** to draw the perpendicular bisector of the chord AB.

(e) Similarly, construct the perpendicular bisector of the chord CD.

(f) Drag the end points of the chords and observe the intersecting point of the two perpendicular bisectors.

Question

1. Suggest a property of the perpendicular bisector of a chord of a circle.

Class Activity 1 reveals the following property.

> The perpendicular bisector of a chord of a circle passes through the centre of the circle.
> (Abbreviation: ⊥ bisector of chord)

In the diagram, PQ is the perpendicular bisector of the chord AB of the circle. Then the centre O is on the line PQ. ($\perp$ bisector of chord)

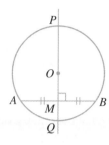

This property enables us to locate the centre of a circle. The diagram below shows a tracing of a broken circular plate. We locate the centre (and hence determine the radius) of the plate by marking three points A, B and C on it and drawing the perpendicular bisectors of AB and BC. The intersecting point of the perpendicular bisectors is the centre.

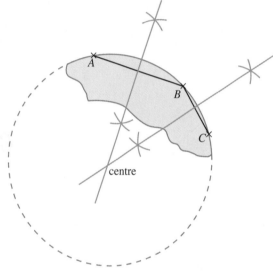

Example 1   In the diagram, M is the midpoint of the chord AB, and PQ is the perpendicular bisector of AB. $AB = 8$ cm and $MQ = 2$ cm. Find the radius of the circle.

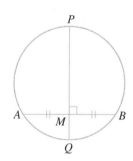

Solution   Let r cm be the radius of the circle.

The centre O lies on the line PQ.
($\perp$ bisector of chord)

Join OB as shown in the diagram.

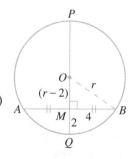

$$
\begin{aligned}
OB^2 &= OM^2 + MB^2 \quad &\text{(Pythagoras' Theorem)}\\
r^2 &= (r-2)^2 + 4^2 \quad &(OM = OQ - MQ)\\
r^2 &= r^2 - 4r + 4 + 16\\
4r &= 20\\
r &= 5
\end{aligned}
$$

The radius of the circle is 5 cm.

▶ *Try It 1!*   In the diagram, *M* is the midpoint of the chord *CD*, and *HK* is the perpendicular bisector of *CD*. *CD* = 30 cm and *MK* = 9 cm. Find the radius of the circle.

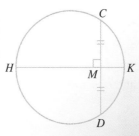

Class Activity 2

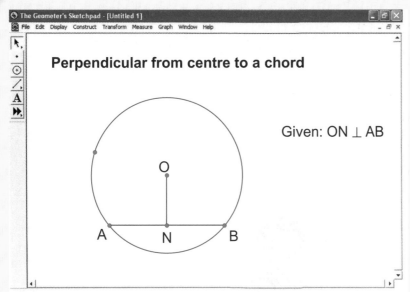

From Class Activity 1, we learnt that the perpendicular bisector of a chord of a circle passes through the centre of the circle. Let us consider the reverse case by drawing the perpendicular from the centre *O* of a circle to a chord.

Tasks

(a) Construct a circle with centre *O*.

(b) Draw a chord *AB* of the circle.

(c) Construct the perpendicular line from *O* to the chord *AB*.

(d) Mark the intersecting point *N* of the perpendicular line and the chord *AB*.

(e) Select the points *O* and *N*, and then select the menu **Construct | Segment** to draw the line segment *ON*.

(f) Hide the perpendicular line. You should get the diagram as shown at the beginning of this activity.

(g) Measure the lengths of *AN* and *BN*.

(h) Drag the point *A* and observe the changes in the lengths of *AN* and *BN*.

Question

1. What can you say about the lengths of *AN* and *BN*?

From the above class activity, we can conclude that:

> The perpendicular from the centre of a circle to a chord bisects the chord.
> (Abbreviation: ⊥ from centre bisects chord)

In the diagram, $ON \perp AB$.
Then $AN = BN$. (⊥ from centre bisects chord)

Refer to Class Activity 1 and Class Activity 2. Reflect on how both these activities are related.

Example 2 In the diagram, *AB* and *CD* are two parallel chords of a circle, centre *O*. $AB = 30$ cm, $CD = 48$ cm and the perpendicular distance from *O* to *AB* is 20 cm. Find
(a) the radius of the circle,
(b) the perpendicular distance between *AB* and *CD*.

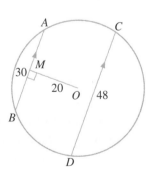

Solution   (a) Draw the radii OA and OC. Draw the perpendicular ON from O to CD. Since $AB \parallel CD$, MON is a straight line.

In $\triangle OAM$,

$$AM = \frac{1}{2} AB \qquad (\perp \text{ from centre}$$
$$\qquad\qquad\qquad\qquad \text{bisects chord})$$
$$= \frac{1}{2} \times 30$$
$$= 15 \text{ cm}$$
$$OA^2 = AM^2 + OM^2 \qquad (\text{Pythagoras' Theorem})$$
$$OA = \sqrt{625}$$
$$= 25 \text{ cm}$$

The radius of the circle is 25 cm.

(b) In $\triangle OCN$,

$$CN = \frac{1}{2} CD \qquad (\perp \text{ from centre bisects chord})$$
$$= \frac{1}{2} \times 48$$
$$= 24 \text{ cm}$$
$$OC^2 = CN^2 + ON^2 \qquad (\text{Pythagoras' Theorem})$$
$$25^2 = 24^2 + ON^2$$
$$ON^2 = 49$$
$$ON = 7 \text{ cm}$$

Perpendicular distance between AB and $CD = MO + ON$
$$= 20 + 7$$
$$= 27 \text{ cm}$$

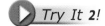 *Try It 2!*   In the diagram, AB and CD are two parallel chords of a circle, centre O. $AB = 24$ cm, $CD = 16$ cm and $OM = 5$ cm. Find
(a) the radius of the circle,
(b) the distance between M and N.

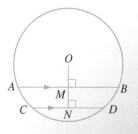

Two chords are equal if they are of equal length. In the diagram, PQ and RS are two equal chords of a circle. What can you say about the perpendicular distances of the centre O from PQ and RS?

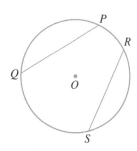

Class Activity 3

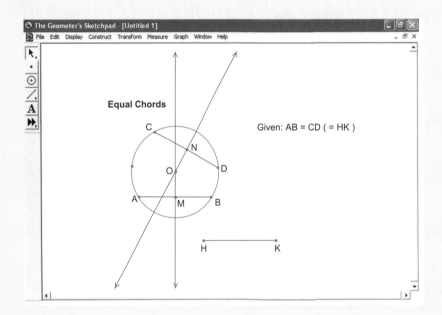

Tasks

Do the following using Sketchpad.
(a) Draw a circle with centre O.
(b) Draw a line segment HK at the bottom part of the sketch space. It will be used to vary the lengths of equal chords.
(c) Mark a point A on the circle. Click A and HK, and then select **Construct | Circle by center + Radius** to draw a circle with centre A and radius HK to cut the circle at B.
(d) Construct the chord AB and hide the circle drawn in Step **(c)**.
(e) Mark a point C on the circle. Construct a chord CD with its length equal to HK using Step **(c)** and Step **(d)**.
(f) Draw the perpendicular lines from O to the chords AB and CD. Mark the midpoints M and N of the chords. The resulting diagram will be as shown above.
(g) Measure the lengths of AB, CD, OM and ON.
(h) Drag the points H, K, A or C and observe the changes in AB, CD, OM and ON.

Question

1.   What is the common property of the equal chords, AB and CD?

From the Class Activity 3, we can derive the following property.

Equal chords of a circle are equidistant from the centre of the circle.
(Abbreviation: equal chords, equidistant from centre)

Geometric patterns involving circles have been used in art for many centuries. Some beautiful examples of such patterns can be found in Islamic art and Tibetan mandalas.

In the diagram, $AB = CD$.
Then $\qquad OM = ON$. (equal chords, equidistant from centre)

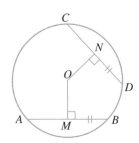

Example 3   In the diagram, O is the centre of the circle, $AB = CD$ and $OM = 10$ cm. Find the length of ON.

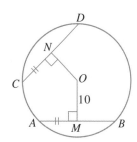

Solution $AB = CD$ (given)
$\qquad \therefore\ ON = OM$ (equal chords, equidistant from centre)
$\qquad\qquad\quad = 10$ cm

▶ *Try It 3!*   In the diagram, O is the centre of the circle, $AB = CD$ and $ON = 7$ cm. Find the length of OM.

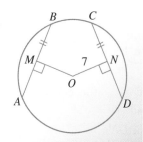

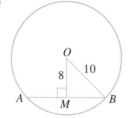

Exercise 6.1

In this exercise, *O* is the centre of a circle and the unit of length is cm.

Basic Practice

1. Find the length of the chord *AB* in each of the following.

   (a)

   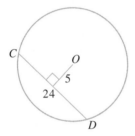

   (b)

   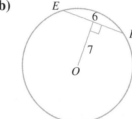

2. Find the radius of each circle.

   (a)

   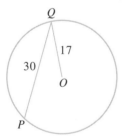

   (b)

   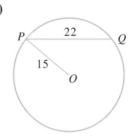

3. Find the perpendicular distance from the centre *O* to the chord *PQ* in each circle.

   (a)

   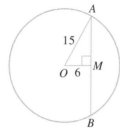

   (b)

   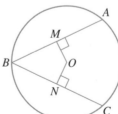

Further Practice

4. In the diagram, *O* is the centre of the circle. *AB* = *BC* = 80 cm and *OM* = 9 cm. Find
   (a) the length of *ON*,
   (b) the radius of the circle.

5. In the diagram, *AB* and *CD* are parallel chords of the circle with centre *O*. *AB* = 5 cm, *CD* = 4 cm and the radius of the circle is 3 cm. Find the perpendicular distance between the two chords. (Give your answer correct to 3 significant figures.)

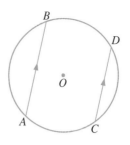

6. In the diagram, *O* is the centre of the two concentric circles and *ABCD* is a straight line. *BC* = 30 cm, and the radii of the two circles are 25 cm and 29 cm, respectively.

(a) Is *AB* = *CD*? Why?

(b) Find the length of
    (i)   *OM*,   (ii) *AD*,
    (iii) *CD*.

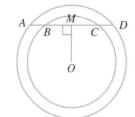

7. In the diagram, the chord *AB* is perpendicular to the diameter *CD*, *AB* = 70 cm and *CE* = 25 cm. Find

(a) the radius of the circle,

(b) the area of △*AOB*, where *O* is the centre of the circle.

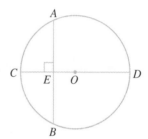

(**Maths@Work**)

8. The diagram shows a fragment of a circular plate.

(a) Trace the diagram.

(b) Find the centre of the plate using a ruler and a pair of compasses.

(c) Find the radius of the plate.

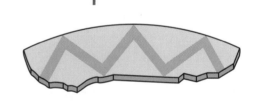

9. The cross-section of a tunnel is in the form of a major segment *ATB* of a circle with centre *O* as shown. The chord *AB* is 8 m long. The perpendicular distance from the highest point *T* to the chord *AB* is 8 m. Find the radius of the cross-section of the tunnel.

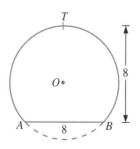

10. The cross-section of a piece of watermelon is in the form of a minor segment *PBQ* of a circle. The chord *PQ* is 24 cm long. The lowest point *B* is 7 cm from the chord *PQ*. Find the radius of the arc *PBQ*.

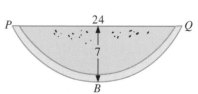

11. In the diagram, *AB* and *CD* are two equal chords of the circle with centre *O*. Name three pairs of congruent triangles.

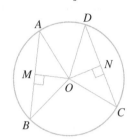

12. *AB* and *CD* are two parallel chords of a circle of radius 15 cm. If *AB* = 24 cm and *CD* = 10 cm, find two possible perpendicular distances between *AB* and *CD*.

6.2 Angles In A Circle

A. Angle at the Centre and Angle at the Circumference

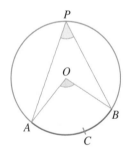   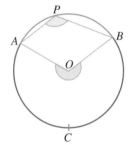

In each of the above figures, the arc *ACB* subtends an angle *AOB* at the centre of the circle and an angle *APB* at the circumference of the circle *ACB*. The angle *AOB* is called the **angle at the centre** subtended by the arc *ACB* and the angle *APB* is called the **angle at the circumference** subtended by the arc *ACB*. We shall see the relationship between these two angles, *AOB* and *APB*, in the following class activity.

Class Activity 4

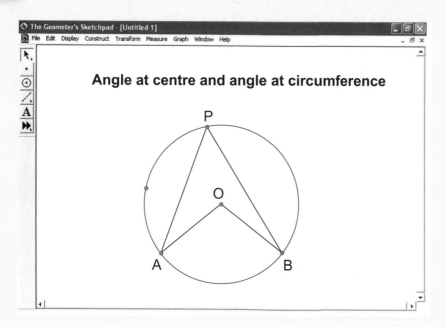

Angle at centre and angle at circumference

Tasks

Do the following using Sketchpad.

(a) Construct a circle with centre O.

(b) Mark three points, A, B and P, on the circle.

(c) Construct the line segments, OA, OB, AP and BP.

(d) Measure the angle at the centre $\angle AOB$, and the angle at the circumference $\angle APB$ subtended by the arc AB.

Questions

1. Calculate the ratio of $\angle AOB$ to $\angle APB$.

2. Drag the point P along the circle. What do you observe?

3. Drag the point A or B along the circle. What do you observe?

4. Suggest a relationship between $\angle AOB$ and $\angle APB$.

Class Activity 4 reveals the following property.

> The angle subtended by an arc at the centre of a circle is twice the angle subtended by the same arc at the circumference.
> (Abbreviation: $\angle$ at centre = $2\angle$ at circumference)

In the diagram, O is the centre of the circle.

$\angle AOB = 2\angle APB$ ($\angle$ at centre = $2\angle$ at circumference)

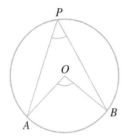

Example 4   In the diagram, O is the centre of the circle and $\angle APB = 47°$. Find $\angle AOB$.

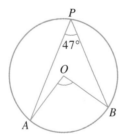

Solution $\angle AOB = 2\angle APB$ ($\angle$ at centre = $2\angle$ at circumference)
$= 2 \times 47°$
$= 94°$

▶ *Try It 4!*   In the diagram, O is the centre of the circle and $\angle AOB = 110°$. Find $\angle APB$.

Example 5 In the diagram, O is the centre of the circle and $\angle AOB = 118°$. Find $\angle APB$.

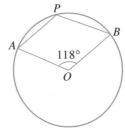

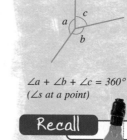

$\angle a + \angle b + \angle c = 360°$
($\angle$s at a point)

Recall

Solution

reflex $\angle AOB = 360° - 118°$ ($\angle$s at a point)
$\qquad\qquad\quad = 242°$

reflex $\angle AOB = 2\angle APB$ ($\angle$ at centre $= 2\angle$ at circumference)
$\qquad\quad 242° = 2\angle APB$
$\therefore \qquad \angle APB = 121°$

Note: Reflex $\angle AOB$ and $\angle APB$ are the angle at the centre and the angle at the circumference subtended by the major arc AB respectively. $\angle AOB$ is not the corresponding angle at the centre for $\angle APB$.

▶ *Try It 5!* In the diagram, O is the centre of the circle and $\angle APB = 130°$. Find $\angle AOB$.

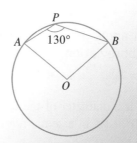

Example 6 In the diagram, O is the centre of the circle, $\angle ABC = 39°$ and $\angle BCO = 25°$. Find $\angle ADC$.

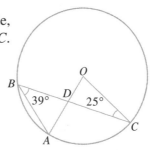

Solution

$\angle AOC = 2\angle ABC$ ($\angle$ at centre $= 2\angle$ at circumference)
$\qquad\quad = 2 \times 39°$
$\qquad\quad = 78°$
$\angle ADC = \angle AOC + \angle DCO$ (ext. $\angle$ of $\triangle$)
$\qquad\quad = 78° + 25°$
$\qquad\quad = 103°$

Note: $\angle AOC$ is the corresponding angle at the centre for $\angle ABC$ as both angles are subtended by the minor arc AC.

▶ *Try It 6!* In the diagram, O is the centre of the circle. PR and OQ intersect at right angles at S, and $\angle OPS = 22°$. Find $\angle PRQ$.

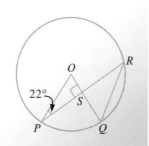

B. Angle in a Semicircle

In the diagram, *AOB* is a diameter of the circle with centre *O*. Then ∠*AOB* and ∠*APB* are the angle at the centre and the angle at the circumference subtended by the semicircular arc *ACB* respectively. Since segment *APB* is a semicircle, ∠*APB* is called an **angle in a semicircle**.

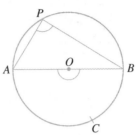

Now,　∠*APB* = $\frac{1}{2}$ ∠*AOB*　　(∠ at centre = 2∠ at circumference)

　　　　　= $\frac{1}{2}$ × 180°　(st. ∠)

　　　　　= 90°

Thus, we have the following property.

> An angle in a semicircle is a right angle.
> (Abbreviation: ∠ in a semicircle)

In the diagram, *AOB* is a diameter of the circle.
Then　∠*APB* = 90°.　(∠ in a semicircle)

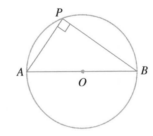

Example 7　In the diagram, *AB* is a diameter of the circle with centre *O*, *AB // DC* and ∠*AOD* = 56°. Find ∠*ABC*.

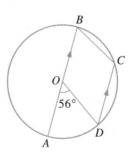

Solution　Join *A* and *C*.

∠*x* = $\frac{1}{2}$ ∠*AOD*　　(∠ at centre = 2∠ at circumference)

　　= $\frac{1}{2}$ × 56°

　　= 28°

∠*y* = 90°　　　　(∠ in a semicircle)

∠*x* + ∠*y* + ∠*z* = 180°　　　(int. ∠s, *AB // DC*)

∴　　∠*z* = 180° − 28° − 90°

　　　　 = 62°

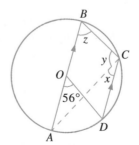

▶ *Try It **7!***   In the diagram, $AD \parallel OC$, AB is a diameter of the circle with centre O, and $\angle OCD = 57°$. Find $\angle BOC$.

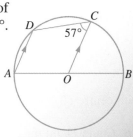

C. Angles in the Same Segment

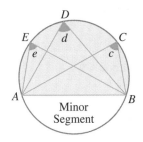
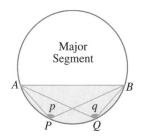

In each of the above diagrams, the chord AB divides a circle into a major segment and a minor segment. $\angle c$, $\angle d$ and $\angle e$ are angles subtended at the circumference by the chord AB on the major segment $AEDCB$. They are called **angles in the same segment**. Similarly, $\angle p$ and $\angle q$, being subtended by AB on the minor segment $APQB$, are a pair of angles in the same segment.

Class Activity 5

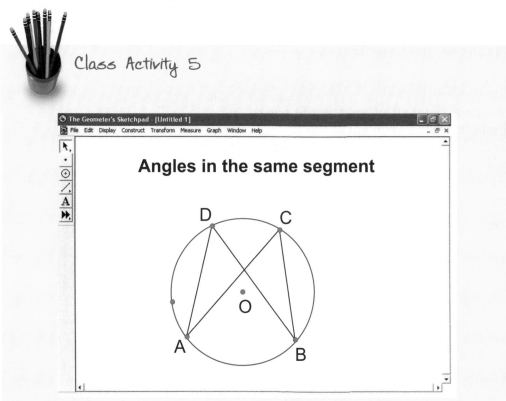

Let us study the property of angles in the same segment using Sketchpad.

Tasks

(a) Construct a circle with centre O.

(b) Mark the points, A, B, C and D, on the circumference of the circle.

(c) Join the line segments, AC, BC, AD and BD.

(d) Measure $\angle ACB$ and $\angle ADB$.

Questions

1. Drag the point C along the major segment AB. What do you observe about the sizes of these two angles?

2. Drag point A or B around. What do you observe about the sizes of $\angle ACB$ and $\angle ADB$?

3. Drag both points C and D to the minor segment AB. What do you observe about the sizes of $\angle ACB$ and $\angle ADB$?

4. Suggest a property of the angles in the same segment.

From the above class activity, we observe the following property.

The angles in the same segment of a circle are equal.
(Abbreviation: $\angle$s in the same segment)

In the diagram, we have

$$\angle ACB = \angle ADB. \quad (\angle\text{s in the same segment})$$

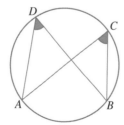

Example 8
In the diagram, AC and BD intersect at E, $\angle ADB = 45°$ and $\angle AEB = 85°$. Find $\angle CBD$.

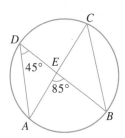

Solution

$\begin{aligned} \angle ACB &= \angle ADB &&\text{($\angle$s in the same segment)}\\ &= 45° \end{aligned}$

$\begin{aligned} \angle CBD + \angle ACB &= \angle AEB &&\text{(ext. $\angle$ of $\triangle$)}\\ \angle CBD + 45° &= 85° \\ \therefore \qquad \angle CBD &= 40° \end{aligned}$

▶ *Try It* **8!**
In the diagram, AC and BD intersect at E, $\angle ACB = 54°$ and $\angle ABD = 53°$. Find $\angle ADB$ and $\angle DAB$.

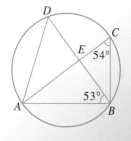

Example 9
In the diagram, O is the centre of the circle and AC is a diameter. AED and BCD are straight lines, AC and BE intersect at F, $\angle CDE = 26°$, and $\angle CAE = 18°$. Find $\angle x$ and $\angle y$.

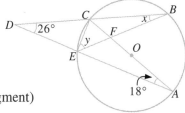

Solution

$\begin{aligned} \angle x &= \angle CAE &&\text{($\angle$s in the same segment)}\\ &= 18° \end{aligned}$

$\begin{aligned} \angle AEB &= \angle CDE + \angle x &&\text{(ext. $\angle$ of $\triangle$)}\\ &= 26° + 18° \\ &= 44° \end{aligned}$

$\begin{aligned} \angle y + \angle AEB &= 90° &&\text{($\angle$ in a semicircle)}\\ \angle y + 44° &= 90° \\ \therefore \qquad \angle y &= 46° \end{aligned}$

▶ *Try It* **9!**
In the diagram, O is the centre of the circle and BE is a diameter. ABC and EDC are straight lines, AD and BE intersect at F, $\angle BCD = 28°$, and $\angle BED = 25°$. Find $\angle x$ and $\angle y$.

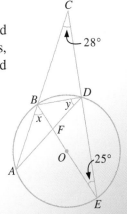

6

Exercise 6.2

In each of the diagrams, *O* is the centre of the given circle.

Basic Practice

1. Find the marked angle *x* in each diagram.

   (a)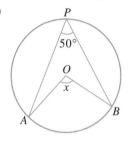

   (b)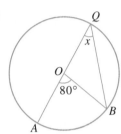

   (c)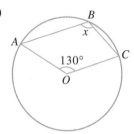

   (d)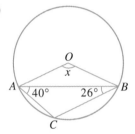

2. Find the marked angle *y* in each diagram, where *AB* is a diameter.

   (a)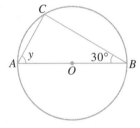

   (b)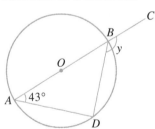

   (c)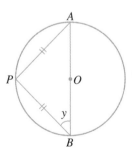

   (d)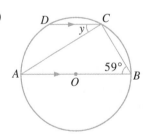

3. Find the marked angle z in each diagram.

(a)

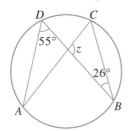

(b)

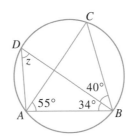

(c)

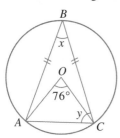

(d)

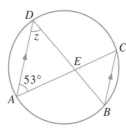

(**Further Practice**)

4. Find the marked angles, x and y, in each diagram.

(a)

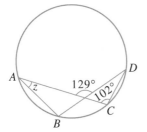

(b)

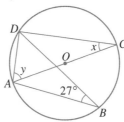

(c)

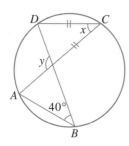

(d)

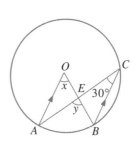

5. In the figure, AB is a diameter of the circle with centre O. ABC and CDE are straight lines, AD and BE intersect at F, $\angle DAB = 18°$, and $\angle BCD = 20°$. Find $\angle DBE$.

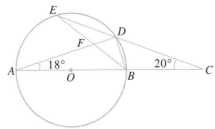

6. In the diagram, *ABC* and *CDE* are straight lines, ∠*DAE* = 45°, ∠*ABE* = 50°, and ∠*BDC* = 66°. Find ∠*BCD*.

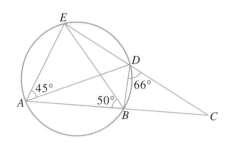

---

7. The diagram shows a semicircular field. *AB* = 34 m and *AP* = 16 m. Find
    (a) the length of *BP*,
    (b) the area of △*APB*,
    (c) the perpendicular distance from *P* to *AB*,
    (d) the perpendicular distance from the centre *O* to *AP*.

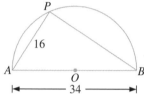

8. In the diagram, *AD* and *BC* are two equal chords of the circle. *AC* and *BD* intersect at *E*, and ∠*AEB* = 70°.
    (a) State why △*AED* ≡ △*BEC*.
    (b) Is *AE* equal to *BE*?
    (c) Find ∠*EAB*.

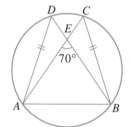

9. In the diagram, the chords *AC* and *BD* intersect at *E*, *AE* = 12 cm, *DE* = 10 cm, *BE* = 20 cm, and *CE* = *x* cm.
    (a) Name a pair of similar triangles in the diagram and state the reason for the similarity.
    (b) Hence find the value of *x*.

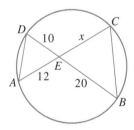

---

10. In the diagram, the width of the goal post, *AB*, of a football field subtends an angle of 30° at the football *F*.
    (a) Plot four other positions of *F* such that ∠*AFB* = 30°.
    (b) Describe all the possible positions of *F* such that ∠*AFB* = 30° in front of the goal post *AB*.

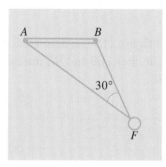

6.3 Angles In The Opposite Segments

We learnt that the angles in the same segment are equal. Is there any relationship between the angles in the opposite segments of a circle?

Class Activity 6

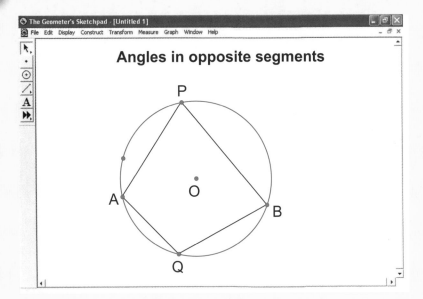

Tasks

Do the following using Sketchpad.

(a) Construct a circle with centre O.

(b) Construct a quadrilateral $AQBP$ on the circle.

(c) Measure $\angle APB$ and $\angle AQB$.

(d) Calculate the sum of the two angles.

Questions

1. Drag the point P around. What do you observe about $\angle APB$ and $\angle AQB$?

2. Drag point A around. What do you observe about these two angles?

3. Suggest a relationship between $\angle APB$ and $\angle AQB$.

From Class Activity 6, we observe the following.

> The sum of the angles in the opposite segments of a circle is 180°.
> (Abbreviation: ∠s in opp. segments)

In the diagram, we have

$$\angle APB + \angle AQB = 180°. \quad (\angle s \text{ in opp. segments})$$

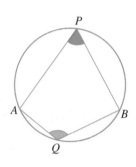

Example 10   In the diagram, $\angle BAD = 65°$ and $\angle BDC = 35°$. Find $\angle x$.

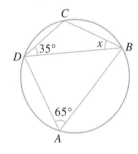

*The quadrilateral ABCD with its four vertices on the circumference of a circle is called a **cyclic quadrilateral**.*

Solution

$$\begin{aligned}
\angle BCD + \angle BAD &= 180° \quad (\angle s \text{ in opp. segments}) \\
\angle BCD + 65° &= 180° \\
\angle BCD &= 115° \\
\angle x + \angle BCD + \angle BDC &= 180° \quad (\angle \text{ sum of } \triangle) \\
\angle x + 115° + 35° &= 180° \\
\angle x &= 30°
\end{aligned}$$

▶ *Try It 10!*   In the diagram, $\angle BAC = 55°$ and $\angle ACB = 48°$. Find $\angle y$.

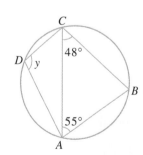

Example 11 In the diagram, AB is a diameter of the circle with centre O and $\angle AED = 128°$. Find $\angle x$.

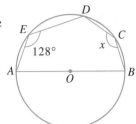

Solution Construct the line segment AC.

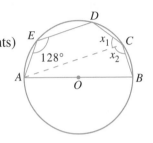

$$\angle x_1 + \angle AED = 180° \quad (\angle \text{s in opp. segments})$$
$$\angle x_1 + 128° = 180°$$
$$\angle x_1 = 52°$$
$$\angle x_2 = 90° \quad (\angle \text{ in a semicircle})$$
$$\therefore \quad \angle x = \angle x_1 + \angle x_2$$
$$= 52° + 90°$$
$$= 142°$$

Try It 11! In the diagram, AB is a diameter of the circle with centre O and $\angle BAD = 60°$. Find $\angle y$.

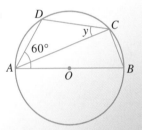

Example 12 In the diagram, ABC and DEF are straight lines, and $\angle BAF = 100°$. Find $\angle x$.

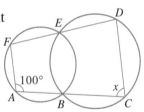

Solution Join B and E.

$$\angle y + \angle BAF = 180° \quad (\angle \text{s in opp. segments})$$
$$\angle y + 100° = 180°$$
$$\angle y = 80°$$
$$\angle y + \angle z = 180° \quad (\text{adj. } \angle \text{s on a st. line})$$
$$80° + \angle z = 180°$$
$$\angle z = 100°$$
$$\angle x + \angle z = 180° \quad (\angle \text{s in opp. segments})$$
$$\angle x + 100° = 180°$$
$$\angle x = 80°$$

Discuss

AF is parallel to CD. Why?

Try It 12! In the diagram, ABC and DEF are straight lines, and $\angle CDE = 70°$. Find $\angle t$.

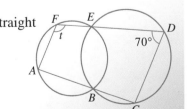

Exercise 6.3

In each of the diagrams in this exercise, *O* is the centre of the given circle.

1. Find the marked unknown angles in each of the following.

(a)

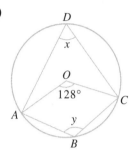

(b) *BCE* is a straight line.

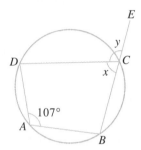

(c)

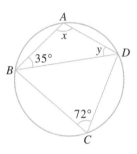

(d)

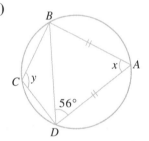

(e)

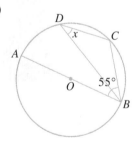

(f)

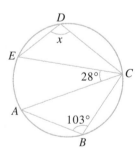

(g)

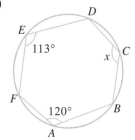

(h)

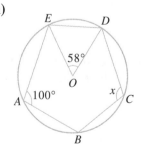

Further Practice

2. In the diagram, $\angle CAB = 46°$ and $\angle ABC = 72°$. Find
    (a) $\angle ADC$,
    (b) $\angle ADB$.

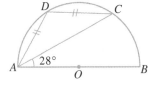

3. The diagram shows a semicircle with $\angle BAC = 28°$, and $AD = CD$. Find
    (a) $\angle ADC$,
    (b) $\angle ACD$.

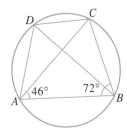

4. In the diagram, ABC and AED are straight lines. $\angle ABE = 80°$ and $\angle ACD = 68°$. Find $\angle x$.

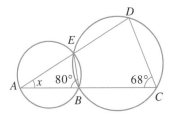

5. In the diagram, ABC and DEF are straight lines. $\angle BAF = 75°$ and $\angle AFE = 77°$. Find
    (a) $\angle x$,
    (b) $\angle y$.

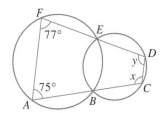

6. In the diagram, ABE, ADF, BCF and DCE are straight lines. $\angle AED = 30°$ and $\angle AFB = 34°$. Find $\angle x$.

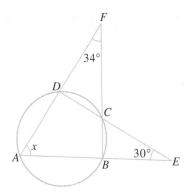

Maths@Work

7. In the diagram, AB is a diameter of the circle with centre O, $BC = BD$ and $\angle BAC = 25°$.
    (a) Name a pair of congruent triangles and state the reason for the congruence.
    (b) Hence find $\angle CBD$.

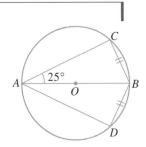

8. In the diagram, $AB \parallel DC$, $AB = 18$ cm, $DC = 8$ cm, $AD = 13$ cm and $\angle BAD = \theta$.

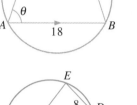

   (a) Show that $\angle ABC = \theta$.
   (b) Is $BC = AD$? Why?
   (c) Find the perpendicular distance between AB and DC.
   (d) Find the area of the quadrilateral $ABCD$.

9. In the diagram, ABC and CDE are straight lines. $AB = 20$ cm, $CD = 16$ cm, $DE = 8$ cm and $\angle BAE = \theta$.

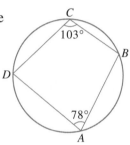

   (a) Show that $\angle BDC = \theta$.
   (b) Name a pair of similar triangles and state the reason for the similarity.
   (c) Hence find the length of BC.

Brainworks

10. Point out the mistake in the diagram. Suggest one or more possible amendments.

6.4 Tangents To A Circle

A. Tangent at a Point

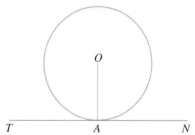

A circle is itself a curve. Therefore, at each point on the circumference of a circle, we can draw a tangent to touch the circle at that point. In the above diagram, TAN is the tangent to the circle at A.

By the symmetry of the diagram,
$$\angle OAT = \angle OAN$$
$$\angle OAT + \angle OAT = 180° \quad \text{(adj. } \angle \text{s on a st. line)}$$
$$\therefore \ \angle OAN = \angle OAT = 90°.$$

Hence we have the following property.

> A tangent to a circle is perpendicular to the radius of the circle
> drawn from the point of contact.
> (Abbreviation: tangent ⊥ radius)

In the diagram, *TAN* is the tangent to the circle at *A*.
Then $\quad OA \perp TN$. (tangent ⊥ radius)

Note: A tangent to a circle touches the circle at
only one point.

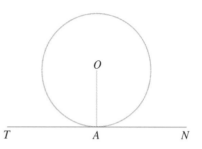

Example 13 In the diagram, *O* is the centre of the circle,
TN is the tangent to the circle at *A* and
$\angle BAT = 35°$. Find
(a) $\angle AOB$,
(b) $\angle APB$.

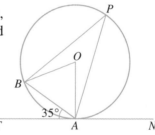

*Stonehenge, a famous
megalithic ruin in Britain,
is an ancient monument of
giant stones forming
concentric circles, of
which two are left
standing today.
Researchers are still
trying to determine who
built this monument and
why it was built.*

Solution **(a)** $\quad \angle OAT = 90°$ $\qquad$ (tangent ⊥ radius)
$$\angle OAB = \angle OAT - \angle BAT$$
$$= 90° - 35°$$
$$= 55°$$

$\qquad OA = OB$ $\qquad$ (radii of the same circle)
$\therefore \angle OBA = \angle OAB$ $\qquad$ (base ∠s of isos. △)
$$= 55°$$

$$\angle AOB = 180° - \angle OAB - \angle OBA \quad (\angle \text{ sum of } \triangle)$$
$$= 180° - 55° - 55°$$
$$= 70°$$

(b) $\angle APB = \dfrac{1}{2} \times \angle AOB$ $\quad$ (∠ at centre = 2∠ at circumference)

$$= \frac{1}{2} \times 70°$$
$$= 35°$$

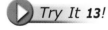 *Try It 13!* In the diagram, *O* is the centre of the circle.
TN is the tangent to the circle at *A* and
$\angle BAT = 40°$. Find
(a) $\angle AOB$,
(b) $\angle APB$.

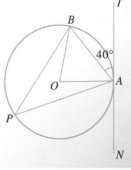

Example 14 In the diagram, *TA* is the tangent to the circle, centre *O*, at *A*. *AT* = 10 cm and *BT* = 7 cm. Find the radius of the circle.

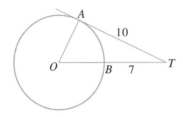

Solution Let *r* cm be the radius of the circle.

$$\angle OAT = 90° \qquad \text{(tangent} \perp \text{radius)}$$
$$OT^2 = OA^2 + AT^2 \qquad \text{(Pythagoras' Theorem)}$$
$$(r + 7)^2 = r^2 + 10^2$$
$$r^2 + 14r + 49 = r^2 + 100$$
$$14r = 51$$
$$r = \frac{51}{14}$$
$$= 3\frac{9}{14}$$

∴ the radius of the circle is $3\dfrac{9}{14}$ cm.

▷ *Try It 14!* In the diagram, *TA* is the tangent to the circle, centre *O*, at *A*. *BT* = 4 cm and *AT* = 6 cm. Find the radius of the circle.

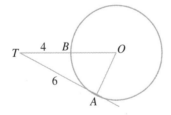

B. Tangents from an External Point

Refer to Example 14. In fact, we can draw another tangent from the external point *T* to the circle. The two tangents from *T* have some interesting relationships which we will find out through the following class activity.

Class Activity 7

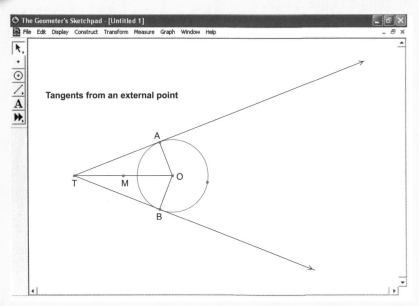

Let us see how to draw the tangents from an external point to a circle and investigate their properties using Sketchpad.

Tasks

(a) Construct a circle with centre O.

(b) Mark a point T outside the circle and construct the line segment OT.

(c) Construct the midpoint M of OT and the line segment OM.

(d) Construct the circle with centre M and radius OM.

(e) Construct the rays TA and TB from T to the intersecting points of the two circles, A and B.

(f) Hide the circle constructed in Step **(d)**.

(g) Construct the line segments OA and OB. You should get the diagram as shown above, and TA and TB are tangents to the circle at A and B respectively.

(h) Measure the lengths of AT and BT, and the angles $\angle OAT$, $\angle OBT$, $\angle ATO$, $\angle BTO$, $\angle AOT$ and $\angle BOT$.

(i) Drag the point T around and observe the variation in the measurements.

There is reflection symmetry of the figure about the line OT.

Remark

Question

1. Suggest some properties of the tangents from an external point.

From Class Activity 7, we observe the following property.

> If two tangents are drawn from an external point to a circle, then
> - the lengths of the tangents are equal,
> - the line joining the external point and the centre bisects the angle between the tangents.
>
> (Abbreviation: tangents from ext. point)

In the diagram, *TA* and *TB* are tangents from *T* to the circle at *A* and *B* respectively.

Then   1.   *TA* = *TB*,   (tangents from ext. point)
             2.   ∠*ATO* = ∠*BTO*.

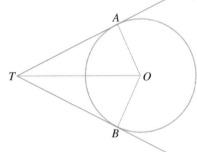

Example 15   In the diagram, the circle *PQR* inscribed in △*ABC* touches the three sides of the triangle. *AB* = 8 cm, *BC* = 12 cm and *AC* = 10 cm. Find the lengths of *AR* and *CP*.

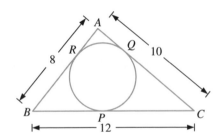

Solution   Let *AR* = *x* cm and *CP* = *y* cm.

$$AQ = AR \qquad \text{(tangents from ext. point)}$$
$$AQ = x \text{ cm}$$

Similarly, *BP* = *BR*   and *CQ* = *CP* (tangents from ext. point)
∴   *BP* = (8 − *x*) cm and *CQ* = *y* cm

Consider the lengths of the sides of *BC* and *CA*.

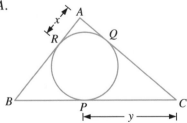

BC: (8 − *x*) + *y* = 12 .... (1)
CA: *x* + *y* = 10 .... (2)

(1) + (2), 8 + 2*y* = 22
            2*y* = 14
             y = 7

Substituting *y* = 7 into (2),
      x + 7 = 10
          x = 3
∴ *AR* = 3 cm and *CP* = 7 cm.

Try It 15! In the diagram, the circle *PQR* is inscribed in △*ABC*, with *AB* = 15 cm, *BC* = 17 cm and *AC* = 12 cm. Find the lengths of *AQ* and *BP*.

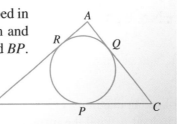

Example 16 In the diagram, *TA* and *TB* are tangents to the circle, centre *O*, at *A* and *B* respectively, and ∠*OTB* = 31°. Find
(a) ∠*TAB*,
(b) ∠*AOB*.

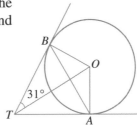

Solution **(a)**

$$∠OTA = ∠OTB \quad \text{(tangents from ext. point)}$$
$$= 31°$$
$$TA = TB \quad \text{(tangents from ext. point)}$$
$$∴ \quad ∠TAB = ∠TBA \quad \text{(base ∠s of isos. △)}$$
$$∠TAB + ∠TBA + ∠ATB = 180° \quad (∠ \text{ sum of △})$$
$$∴ ∠TAB + ∠TAB + 31° + 31° = 180°$$
$$2∠TAB = 118°$$
$$∠TAB = 59°$$

(b)

$$∠TBO = 90° \quad \text{(tangent ⊥ radius)}$$
$$∠OTB + ∠TBO + ∠BOT = 180° \quad (∠ \text{ sum of △})$$
$$31° + 90° + ∠BOT = 180°$$
$$∠BOT = 59°$$

Similarly, in △*OAT*, ∠*AOT* = 59°
Hence

$$∠AOB = ∠AOT + ∠BOT$$
$$= 59° + 59°$$
$$= 118°$$

Try It 16! In the diagram, *TP* and *TQ* are tangents to the circle, centre *O*, at *P* and *Q* respectively, and ∠*POT* = 65°. Find
(a) ∠*PTQ*,
(b) ∠*PQT*.

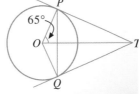

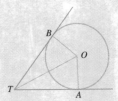

If TA and TB are tangents to the circle with centre O,
∠*OAT* = ∠*OBT* = 90°,
∠*OTA* = ∠*OTB*.

By considering the sum of angles in △*OAT* *and* △*OBT*, *we have*
∠*AOT* = ∠*BOT*.

Remark

Exercise 6.4

Basic Practice

1. In each of the following diagrams, *O* is the centre of the circle and *TAN* is the tangent to the circle at *A*. Find the marked angle *x*.

(a)

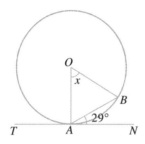

(b)

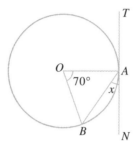

(c)

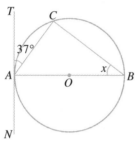

(d)

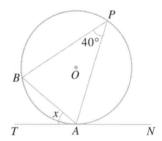

2. In the diagram, *TA* is the tangent to the circle at *A*, the radius *OA* = 6 cm and *TA* = 8 cm. Find the length of *OT*.

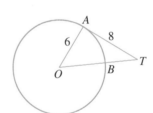

3. In the diagram, *TA* is the tangent to the circle at *A*, *TA* = 5 cm and *TB* = 3 cm. Find the radius *OA* of the circle.

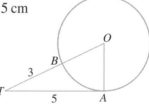

4. In each of the diagrams, *O* is the centre of the circle, *TA* and *TB* are tangents to the circle at *A* and *B* respectively. Find the marked unknown angles.

(a)

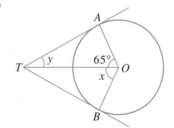

(b)

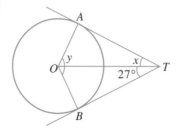

(c)

A

T

x

O 128°

B

(d)

B

O y

x

A 54° T

Further Practice

5. In the diagram, *TA* is the tangent to the circle, centre *O*, at *A*. *OA* = 20 cm, *TA* = 21 cm and ∠*OTA* = 44°. Find
  (a) the length of *OT*,
  (b) ∠*x*.

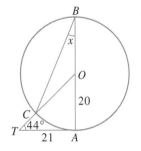

6. In the diagram, *H* and *K* are the centres of two circles whose radii are 3 cm and 5 cm respectively. The two circles touch each other at *C* and *TN* is a common tangent to the circles at *A* and *B*. Find the length of *AB*.

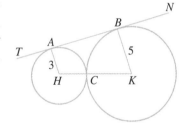

7. In the diagram, the circle touches the sides of △*ABC* at *P*, *Q* and *R*. *AB* = 13 cm, *BC* = 15 cm and *AC* = 12 cm. Find the lengths of *AR* and *CQ*.

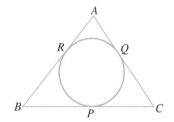

8. In the diagram, the circle touches *AB* produced at *P*, *AC* produced at *R*, and *BC* produced at *Q*. *AB* = 23 cm, *BC* = 17 cm and *AC* = 20 cm. Find the lengths of *AP* and *CQ*.

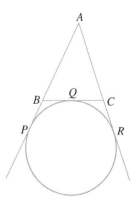

9. In the diagram, the circle touches the sides of △ABC at P, Q and R. ∠BAC = 62° and ∠ABC = 46°. Find ∠x, ∠y and ∠z.

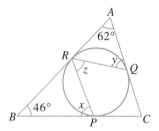

Maths@Work

10. In the figure, a chain is mounted around two wheels, centred at H and K respectively. AB is a common tangent to the wheels. If HK = 30 cm, AH = 12 cm and BK = 5 cm, find the length of AB. Give your answer correct to 3 significant figures.

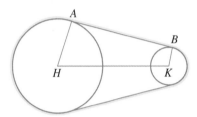

11. In the diagram, four sticks touch a circular disc at P, Q, R and S. Show that AB + CD = BC + AD.

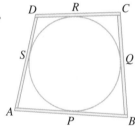

12. The diagram shows a logo. O is the centre of the two concentric circles of radii 30 cm and 15 cm. The chords AB and AC of the larger circle touch the smaller circle at M and N respectively.

(a) State the reason that △OAB is congruent to △OAC.

(b) Find the length of AB, giving your answer correct to 3 significant figures.

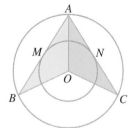

Brainworks

13. Three circles are of radii 1 cm, 2 cm and 3 cm respectively. Draw two possible situations such that the three circles touch each other at only one point.

1. Chords of a Circle

(a)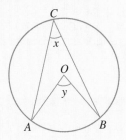

If $PQ \perp AB$ and $AM = BM$, then centre O lies on PQ. ($\perp$ bisector of chord)

(b)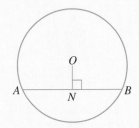

If $ON \perp AB$, then $AN = BN$. ($\perp$ from centre bisects chord)

(c)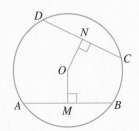

If $AB = CD$, then $OM = ON$. (equal chords, equidistant from centre)

2. Angles in a Circle

(a)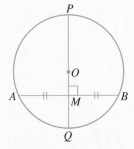

$\angle y = 2\angle x$
($\angle$ at centre
= 2$\angle$ at circumference)

(b)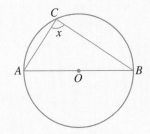

If AB is a diameter, then $\angle x = 90°$. ($\angle$ in a semicircle)

(c)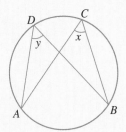

$\angle x = \angle y$
($\angle$s in the same segment)

3. Angles in Opposite Segments

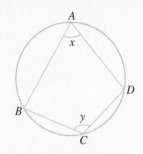

$\angle x + \angle y = 180°$
($\angle$s in opp. segments)

4. Tangents to a Circle

(a)

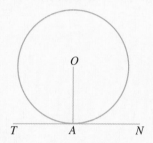

If *TN* is the tangent to the circle at *A*, then *OA* ⊥ *TN*.
(tangent ⊥ radius)

(b)

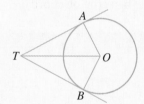

If *TA* and *TB* are tangents to the circle at *A* and *B* respectively,

then   **1.**   *TA* = *TB*,
       2. $\angle ATO = \angle BTO$.
       (tangents from ext. point)

Revision Exercise 6

1. In the diagram, O is the centre of the circle, $AB = CD = 8$ cm and $OM = 3$ cm. Find
    (a) the length of ON,
    (b) the length of AN,
    (c) the radius of the circle.

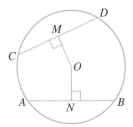

2. In the diagram, AB is a diameter of the circle with centre O. $AC = 24$ cm and $BC = 10$ cm. Find
    (a) the perpendicular distance from O to AC,
    (b) the perpendicular distance from O to BC,
    (c) the radius of the circle.

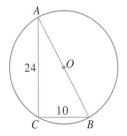

3. In the diagram, AB is a diameter of the circle with centre O, $BC = DC$ and $\angle ABD = 35°$. Find
    (a) $\angle BED$,
    (b) $\angle BCD$,
    (c) $\angle BDC$.

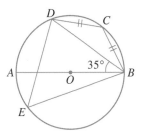

4. In the diagram, $AB \parallel DC$, $\angle DBE = 17°$, $\angle BDC = 43°$ and $\angle AEB = 61°$. Find
    (a) $\angle ABE$,
    (b) $\angle BAE$,
    (c) $\angle BED$.

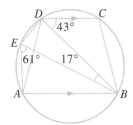

5. In the diagram, AD is a diameter of the circle with centre O. TE is the tangent to the circle at D, $BO \parallel CD$ and $\angle CDE = 54°$. Find
    (a) $\angle CDO$,
    (b) $\angle AOB$,
    (c) $\angle ABC$,
    (d) $\angle BCD$.

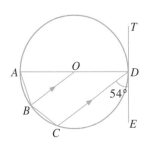

6. In the diagram, *AEF* is a straight line, *AC* // *ED*, ∠*CED* = 32° and ∠*DEF* = 79°. Find

    (a) ∠*ACE*,

    (b) ∠*CBD*,

    (c) ∠*CAE*,

    (d) ∠*DCE*.

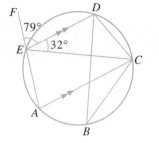
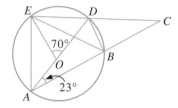

7. In the diagram, *AD* is a diameter of the circle with centre *O*, *ABC* and *CDE* are straight lines, ∠*CAD* = 23°, and ∠*DOE* = 70°. Find

    (a) ∠*DAE*,

    (b) ∠*ADE*,

    (c) ∠*BED*,

    (d) ∠*BCD*.

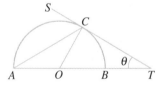

8. In the diagram, *AC* is a diameter of the circle, *ABF* and *DCF* are straight lines, and *AC* and *BD* intersect at *E*. Find

    (a) ∠*BCD*,

    (b) ∠*ABE*,

    (c) ∠*AED*,

    (d) ∠*AFD*.

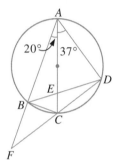

9. In the diagram, *ABT* is a straight line, *TCS* is the tangent to the semicircle with centre *O* at *C*. ∠*BTC* = θ, *BT* = 4 cm and *CT* = 7 cm.

    (a) Express the following angles in terms of θ.

        (i) ∠*BOC*

        (ii) ∠*OAC*

        (iii) ∠*ACS*

    (b) Find the radius of the semicircle.

10. In the diagram, *TA* and *TB* are tangents to the circle with centre *O*, at *A* and *B* respectively. *AB* intersects *OT* at *N* and ∠*OTA* = 29°.

    (a) Name a triangle which is congruent to △*ANT* and state the reason for the congruence.

    (b) Hence find ∠*ANT*.

    (c) Find ∠*NAT*.

    (d) Find ∠*ACN*.

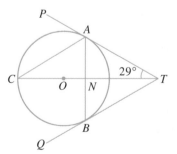

11. The diagram represents the circular cross-section of a road tunnel.

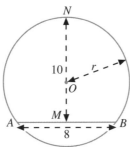

AB represents the horizontal surface of the road. M is the midpoint of AB and is vertically below N, the top of the circle. AB = 8 m and MN = 10 m. The circle has centre O and radius r metres.

(a) Express OM in terms of r. [1]

(b) Form an equation in r and solve it to find the radius of the tunnel. [3]

NP1/2000/18

12. In the diagram, TB is a tangent to the circle, centre O.
TO meets the circle at C and A.
D is another point on the circle.
∠BTC = 22°.

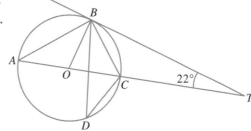

(a) Use the letters in the diagram to name two right angles. [1]

(b) Find
    (i) ∠OAB, [1]
    (ii) ∠ABT, [1]
    (iii) ∠BDC. [1]

NP1/2002/18

13. The points A, B, C and D lie on a circle as shown on Diagram I. AC cuts BD at P. AD is parallel to BC.

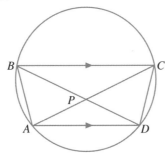

Diagram I

(a) Show that triangle *BPC* is an isosceles triangle. [2]

(b) Given that angle *ACB* = 32° and angle *DAB* = 118°, calculate angle *ACD*. [2]

(c) Diagram II shows the circle in Diagram I and a second circle, centre *O*. The two circles intersect at *C* and *D*.

AD produced cuts the second circle at *F*. BD produced cuts the second circle at *E*. Angle *DEF* = 110°.

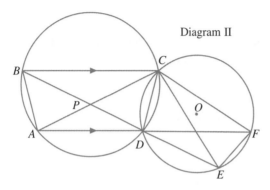

Diagram II

Calculate

(i) angle *ACE*, [3]

(ii) angle *COD*. [2]

NP2/2003/5

14. (a) The diagram shows a circle which passes through *D*, *E* and *F*. *AFB*, *BDC* and *CEA* are tangents to the circle.

D is the midpoint of *BC*.

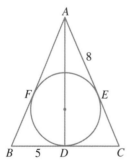

Given that *BD* = 5 cm and *AE* = 8 cm, find

(i) *EC*, [1]

(ii) ∠*CAD*. [2]

(b) The diagram shows a circle which passes through *X*, *Y* and *Z*.
PZQ, *QXR* and *RYP* are tangents to the circle.

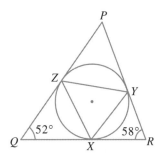

Given that $\angle PQR = 52°$ and $\angle QRP = 58°$, calculate

(i) $\angle QPR$,   [1]

(ii) $\angle QZX$,   [2]

(iii) $\angle ZXY$,   [2]

NP2/2004/5

Extend Your Learning Curve

Centres of Triangles

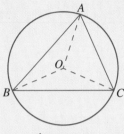

circumcentre

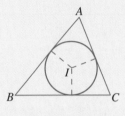

in-centre

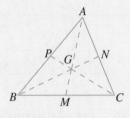

centroid

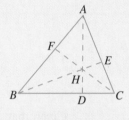

orthocentre

The above diagrams show some centres of a triangle.

(a) Write down the definition of each of these centres.
(*Hint:* Go online to do some research.)

(b) Draw each centre in the case of an obtuse-angled triangle.

(c) Describe some possible relationships of these centres.

Write In Your Journal

Having learnt the properties of circles, would you be able to list some of their practical uses in daily life? One practical use of the circle is the manhole. Do you know why most of the manholes are circular? Try to give an explanation and illustrate with a diagram if necessary.

Problem-Solving Processes and Heuristics

A contemporary mathematician, George Polya (1887–1985), developed a classic four-step problem-solving process to help students become good problem solvers. A summary of the steps from his book *How to Solve It* is given below.

Step 1 Understanding the Problem

(a) Can you restate the problem in your own words?

(b) What are you going to do or what is the goal?

(c) What are the given information and unknowns?

(d) Is there sufficient information or redundant information?

Step 2 Devising a Plan

(a) Find the connection between the given information, unknowns and the goal.

(b) Consider some possible actions or heuristics.

Heuristics are simple and efficient strategies that people use to solve problems. The following is a list of some useful heuristics.

- Use guess and check.
- Draw a diagram.
- Use a variable
- Think of a related problem.
- Work backward.

- Look for a pattern.
- Make a table.
- Write an equation.
- Examine a simpler problem.
- Identify subgoals.

Step 3 Carrying Out the Plan

(a) Implement the strategy or strategies that you have chosen.

(b) Perform the necessary actions or computations.

(c) Modify your plan and choose a new strategy if necessary until the problem is solved.

Step 4 Looking Back

(a) Check that the solution is reasonable and satisfies the original problem.

(b) Examine whether there is another easier method to find the solution.

(c) Extend the solution to solve other problems or more general problems.

We shall illustrate the problem-solving strategies in the following examples.

Example 1

(Use Guess and Check and Make a Table)

Mrs Ho deposits \$3000 into her bank account. The amount \$A$ that she will receive at the end of t months is given by the formula $A = 3000 \times 1.005^t$.

When will the amount be \$3800? Give your answer correct to the nearest integer.

Solution

Step 1 Understanding the Problem

The deposit in Mrs Ho's bank account grows according to the formula
$$A = 3000 \times 1.005^t.$$

We have to find the time t at which
$$3800 = 3000 \times 1.005^t. \quad\text{...............}(1)$$

Step 2 Devising a Plan

Equation (1) is not a linear nor a quadratic equation. We have not learnt the method of solving such an equation.

Therefore we shall use the guess and check method. We substitute different values for t into the right-hand side of the equation and locate the value of t which gives 3800 or is close to 3800.

Step 3 Carrying out the Plan

We use a table to present the work systematically.

t	3000×1.005^t
20	3314.69
30	3484.20
40	3662.38
50	3849.68
45	3754.86
47	3792.50
48	3811.37
47.5	3801.97

This shows that the value of 3000×1.005^t is increasing. When t is greater, it may reach 3800.

Indicates the solution is between $t = 40$ and $t = 50$.

← The solution lies between $t = 45$ and $t = 50$.

The solution lies between $t = 47$ and $t = 48$.

← The solution lies between $t = 47$ and $t = 47.5$.

We locate the solution as shown above.

Since the solution lies between 47 and 47.5, the solution is
$$t = 47 \quad \text{(correct to the nearest integer)}.$$

i.e. the amount will be \$3800 after 47 months.

Step 4 Looking Back

It is more efficient to locate the solution systematically as illustrated in the table rather than by wild guesses.

Alternatively, we can use a spreadsheet program or draw the graph of $A = 3000 \times 1.005^t$ to work out the problem.

We can employ the above technique to solve equations of the form $a^t = b$, where a and b are positive constants.

Note: Students are encouraged to generalise the problem and try to tackle it.

Example 2

(Look for a Pattern and Examine a Simpler Problem)

The following diagram shows a sequence of triangle patterns. The perimeter of triangle ABC is 80 cm. The midpoints of the sides of $\triangle ABC$ are joined to form the second pattern. The midpoints of the sides of the new triangle are joined to form the third pattern and so on. What is the sum of the perimeters of the n triangles in the nth pattern when n is very large?

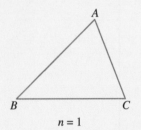
$n = 1$

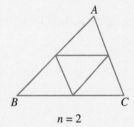
$n = 2$

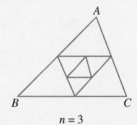
$n = 3$

Solution

Step 1 **Understanding the Problem**

A series of inscribed triangles is formed by joining the midpoints of each preceding triangle. There are n triangles in the nth pattern. We have to find the sum of all the sides of the n triangles in the nth pattern when n is very large.

Step 2 **Devising a Plan**

We shall draw the pattern for $n = 4$ in order to have a better understanding of the patterns.

Before solving the given problem, we examine a simpler problem first: Find the sum of the perimeters of the n triangles when $n =$

(a) 3,

(b) 4,

(c) 10.

Step 3 **Carrying out the Plan**

The diagram below shows the pattern for $n = 4$.

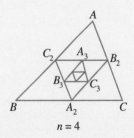
$n = 4$

Note that $\triangle ABC$, $\triangle A_2B_2C_2$, $\triangle A_3B_3C_3$, ... are similar triangles.

and hence $B_2C_2 = \dfrac{1}{2} BC$, $B_3C_3 = \dfrac{1}{2} B_2C_2 = \dfrac{1}{4} BC$, ...

Therefore, perimeter of $\triangle A_2B_2C_2 = \frac{1}{2} \times$ perimeter of $\triangle ABC$

$$= \frac{1}{2} \times 80$$

$$= 40 \text{ cm}$$

Perimeter of $\triangle A_3B_3C_3 = \frac{1}{4} \times$ perimeter of $\triangle ABC$

$$= \frac{1}{4} \times 80$$

$$= 20 \text{ cm}$$

Let S_n be the sum of the perimeters of the n triangles in the nth pattern.

From the above, we have

(a) $S_3 = 80 + 40 + 20$

$\qquad = 140$ cm.

(b) Perimeter of the additional triangle $A_4B_4C_4$ for the 4th pattern

$$= \frac{1}{8} \times 80$$

$= 10$ cm

$\therefore\ S_4 = 80 + 40 + 20 + 10$

$\qquad = 150$ cm

(c) Continuing in this way,

$$S_{10} = 80 + \frac{1}{2} \times 80 + \left(\frac{1}{2}\right)^2 \times 80 + \left(\frac{1}{2}\right)^3 \times 80 + ... + \left(\frac{1}{2}\right)^9 \times 80$$

$$= 159.84 \text{ cm} \quad \text{(correct to 2 d.p.)}.$$

Now, for the case when n is very large, we can observe the pattern of S_n on the following number line.

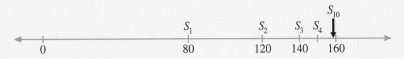

S_2 is the midpoint of S_1 and 160; S_3 is the midpoint of S_2 and 160; S_4 is the midpoint of S_3 and 160; ...; S_{10} is the midpoint of S_9 and 160.

Hence, the sequence S_n approaches 160 as n increases.
$\therefore$ when n is very large, $S_n \approx 160$.
i.e. when n is very large, the sum of the perimeters of the n triangles in the nth pattern is very close to 160 cm.

Step 4 Looking Back
We can verify the answer by using a spreadsheet program to find the values of S_n for $n = 1$ to 1000.

We can generalise the problem to find the sum of the areas of the n triangles in the nth pattern when the area of $\triangle ABC$ is given.

Example 3

(Write an Equation and Identify Subgoals)

A worker lays rectangular bricks to form a pattern as shown in Figure 1. Then he uses 4 bricks to form another pattern as shown in Figure 2. The breadth of a brick is 12 cm. Find the area of the middle hole in Figure 2.

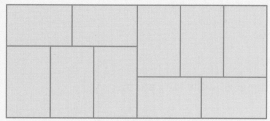

Figure 1

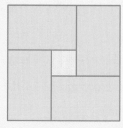

Figure 2

Solution

Step 1 **Understanding the Problem**

In Figure 2, the middle hole is formed by 4 pieces of rectangular bricks. We want to find the area of the hole, given that the breadth of a brick is 12 cm.

Step 2 **Devising a Plan**

In the middle hole, each angle is a right angle and each side is equal to the difference between the length and the breadth of a brick. Therefore, the middle hole is a square.

We are given the breadth of a brick. If we can find the length of a brick, we can find the area of the hole. So we identify a subgoal to find the length of a brick.

From Figure 1, we see that twice the length of a brick is equal to three times its breadth. Hence, we can set up an equation to find the length of a brick and solve the problem.

Step 3 **Carrying Out the Plan**

Let x cm be the length of a brick.

As   twice the length = three times the breadth
$$2x = 3 \times 12$$
$$x = 18$$
i.e. the length of a brick is 18 cm.

Length of a side of the hole $= 18 - 12$
$$= 6 \text{ cm}$$
$\therefore$ area of the hole $= 6^2$
$$= 36 \text{ cm}^2$$

206

Step 4 Looking Back

We can check the solution by calculating the difference between the area of Figure 2 and the total area of 4 bricks.

Area of Figure 2 – total area of 4 bricks
$$= (12 + 18)^2 - 4 \times 12 \times 18$$
$$= 900 - 864$$
$$= 36 \text{ cm}^2$$

An extension of the above problem is to find the area of the middle hole in the diagram below, given that the bricks can be arranged to form the Figure 1 pattern (in the above problem) and the length of each brick is 24 cm.

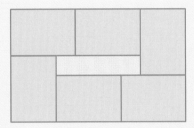

Answers

Chapter 1 Indices

Try It!

1. (a) a^{18} (b) $30x^4y^{11}$
2. (a) q^6 (b) $5rs^7$
3. (a) b^{45} (b) c^{18}
4. (a) $p^{26}q^{26}$ (b) $-a^{14}$
5. (a) $\dfrac{8}{9}$ (b) $\dfrac{1}{125}$
   (c) $\dfrac{1}{8}$ (d) $\dfrac{6}{7}$
6. (a) $\dfrac{m^{20}}{n^{15}}$ (b) $\dfrac{1}{q^5}$ (c) $\dfrac{y^2}{3x}$
7. (a) 2 (b) $\dfrac{4}{5}$
8. (a) 32 (b) $\dfrac{1}{625}$
9. (a) p^2 (b) $\dfrac{y^{\frac{1}{2}}}{x^{\frac{1}{6}}}$
10. (a) 3.78×10^5 (b) 9.2×10^{-5}
11. (a) 79 200 (b) 0.000 026 8
12. (a) 5.09×10^7 (b) 7.649×10^{-13}
13. (a) 3.8×10^8 (b) 1.7×10^{-9}
14. 800
15. 5

Exercise 1.1

1. (a) 3^{12} (b) 2^4 (c) 5^8 (d) 6^{21}
   (e) $4^8 \times 7^8$ (f) $3^8 \times 11^4$ (g) $\dfrac{8^5}{13^5}$ (h) $\dfrac{7^6}{2^{18}}$
2. (a) a^{11} (b) c^3 (c) e^{20} (d) f^{21}
   (e) p^9q^9 (f) r^8s^{12} (g) $\dfrac{t^6}{u^6}$ (h) $\dfrac{v^{55}}{w^{44}}$
3. (a) $15a^8$ (b) $-32b^{12}$ (c) $-4c^3$ (d) $18d^4$
   (e) $16e^{12}$ (f) $16r^{24}s^{16}$ (g) $\dfrac{729u^{12}}{v^6}$ (h) $\dfrac{64x^{21}}{y^{24}}$
4. (a) $a^{12}b^{10}$ (b) c^2d (c) $12e^{11}f^8$ (d) $3g^6h^3$
   (e) $-\dfrac{3}{4}mn^4$ (f) $8p^3q^7$ (g) $-\dfrac{1}{2}s^4t^5$ (h) $u^{21}v^{41}$
   (i) $-w^8x^9$ (j) $8yz^5$
5. (a) $15a^3$ (b) b^8c^{14}
   (c) $\dfrac{250}{3}mn^{10}$ (d) $\dfrac{64}{27}x^4y^{21}$
6. 2^{24} bytes

Exercise 1.2

1. (a) $\dfrac{7}{8}$ (b) 64 (c) $\dfrac{9}{2}$ (d) $\dfrac{1}{64}$
   (e) 1 (f) 1 (g) $\dfrac{1}{3}$ (h) $\dfrac{1}{8}$

2. (a) $\dfrac{1}{a^3}$ (b) $\dfrac{1}{b}$ (c) $\dfrac{9}{e^4}$ (d) $\dfrac{g^6}{f^{10}}$
   (e) $15\,625h^4$ (f) $\dfrac{1}{p^6}$ (g) $\dfrac{s^5}{r^6}$ (h) $\dfrac{x^9}{y^5}$
3. (a) $\dfrac{625}{a^{12}}$ (b) $\dfrac{9}{b}$ (c) $\dfrac{512c^{14}}{d^9}$ (d) $\dfrac{f^7}{e^5}$
   (e) $\dfrac{m^{14}}{n^6}$ (f) $\dfrac{144}{q^6}$ (g) $\dfrac{1}{r^3s^{18}}$ (h) $\dfrac{y^3}{x^2}$
4. $\dfrac{a^9}{t^3}$ units

Exercise 1.3

1. (a) 17 (b) 5 (c) 3
   (d) 3 (e) 1331 (f) 36
   (g) $\dfrac{1}{2}$ (h) $\dfrac{2}{5}$
2. (a) 12 (b) 3 (c) 5
   (d) 2 (e) 343 (f) 625
   (g) $\dfrac{1}{8}$ (h) $\dfrac{1}{121}$ (i) $\dfrac{1}{16}$
   (j) $\dfrac{13}{10}$
3. (a) $a^{\frac{1}{2}}$ (b) $a^{\frac{2}{3}}$ (c) a^2
   (d) $a^{\frac{3}{2}}$ (e) $a^{-\frac{1}{5}}$ (f) $a^{-\frac{3}{4}}$
   (g) $a^{-\frac{5}{2}}$ (h) a^{-4}
4. (a) $a^{\frac{5}{6}}$ (b) $b^{\frac{7}{10}}$ (c) $\dfrac{1}{c^{\frac{3}{8}}}$
   (d) $d^{\frac{8}{3}}$ (e) $\dfrac{e^{\frac{3}{2}}}{f^2}$ (f) $\dfrac{g}{h^{\frac{6}{5}}}$
5. (a) $\dfrac{a^{\frac{8}{3}}}{b^{\frac{1}{6}}}$ (b) $\dfrac{1}{m^{15}}$ (c) $\dfrac{q^{\frac{13}{2}}}{p^{\frac{1}{2}}}$
   (d) $\dfrac{r^{\frac{17}{3}}}{s^{\frac{7}{4}}}$ (e) v (f) $\dfrac{6}{7}p^{\frac{7}{6}}$
   (g) $u^{\frac{1}{6}}$ (h) $\dfrac{1}{2}x^{\frac{5}{9}}y^{\frac{1}{3}}$
6. (a) $x^{\frac{13}{12}}$ cm³ (b) $2(x^{\frac{5}{6}} + x^{\frac{3}{4}} + x^{\frac{7}{12}})$ cm²
   (c) (i) 8192 cm³ (ii) 3328 cm²

Exercise 1.4

1. (a) 8.37×10^4 (b) 7.2×10^5
   (c) 9.62×10^7 (d) 1.45×10^9
   (e) 1.6×10^{-4} (f) 2.8×10^{-5}
   (g) 9.5×10^{-6} (h) 3.0×10^{-8}

2. (a) 9800   (b) 50 000
   (c) 7 230 000   (d) 106 000 000
3. (a) 0.004   (b) 0.000 036
   (c) 0.000 001 58   (d) 0.000 000 000 207
4. (a) 5.06×10^5 (b) 9.068×10^{-7}
   (c) 3.02×10^6 (d) 4.74×10^{-11}
   (e) 1.5×10^{15} (f) 6.8×10^4
   (g) 2.5×10^3 (h) 2×10^{-9}
5. (a) 1.69×10^{14} (b) 1.25×10^{-16}
   (c) 1.4×10^4 (d) 6×10^{-4}
   (e) 3×10^{10} (f) 1.8×10^{-10}
6. 1.76×10^6 kg
7. 1.82×10^{-27} kg
8. (a) 4.01×10^7 m   (b) 0.134 s

Exercise 1.5

1. (a) 5   (b) 6   (c) 3   (d) 3
2. (a) 1   (b) 1   (c) 5   (d) −5
3. 9 hours
4. (a) 9, 3   (b) 3^{-n+7} (c) 14

Revision Exercise 1

1. (a) $x^7 y^3$ (b) $\dfrac{a^2}{b^2}$ (c) $8a^9 b^{12}$ (d) $\dfrac{1}{16q^{11}}$

2. (a) $101\dfrac{1}{100}$ (b) $\dfrac{13}{48}$ (c) $\dfrac{125}{64}$ (d) $\dfrac{3}{2}$

3. (a) $\dfrac{y^4}{x}$ (b) $\dfrac{x^8}{9y^{10}}$ (c) $-288p^7$ (d) $x^{20}y^{18}$

4. (a) 6   (b) 4096   (c) $\dfrac{1}{16}$ (d) $\dfrac{1}{100}$

5. (a) $\dfrac{1}{a^{\frac{11}{6}}}$ (b) $\dfrac{3}{2a^{\frac{13}{12}}}$ (c) $\dfrac{n^{\frac{20}{3}}}{m^3}$ (d) $a-\dfrac{1}{a}$

6. (a) $x = 9.23 \times 10^6$, $y = 4.71 \times 10^5$, $z = 5 \times 10^{-6}$
   (b) (i) 9.701×10^6 (ii) 4.615×10^1
      (iii) 1.25×10^{-16} (iv) 9.42×10^{10}
7. (a) 0.000 000 002 5   (b) 300 000 000
   (c) (i) 2.25×10^8 (ii) 225 000 000
8. (a) 86 400   (b) 3.16×10^7
   (c) 4.73×10^8
9. (a) 9   (b) $\dfrac{3}{2}$

10. (a) 30   (b) 3.97×10^7
11. (a) (i) 0.004 cm   (ii) 4×10^{-5} m
   (b) 0.12 m²
12. (a) $\dfrac{60y}{x}$ km   (b) $n = 3\dfrac{1}{2}$

13. (a) (i) 4.34×10^{10} kg   (ii) 2.8×10^9
   (b) 20%
14. (a) −4, −1.5, −0.3, −0.29, 0
   (b) 1.6×10^{-3} cm
15. (a) $a = 8$ (b) $b = \dfrac{1}{3}$
   (c) $c = -3$
16. (a) 42.5%   (b) 9
17. (a) 6.8×10^{-24} g   (b) 0.612 g

Chapter 2   More about Quadratic Equations

Try It!

1. $x = \dfrac{1}{2}$ or $x = -5$ 2. $x = \dfrac{2}{3}$

3. $x = -\dfrac{3}{5}$ or $x = \dfrac{9}{2}$ 4. $x = -2.6$ or $x = 1.6$

5. $x = -2$ 6. No real roots
7. $x = -5$ or $x = 3$ 8. $x = -1.19$ or $x = 4.19$

9. $x = -2.106$ or $x = 0.356$ 10. $x = -\dfrac{4}{3}$

11. No real roots   12. $x = -1$ or $x = -11$
13. $x = 1$ or $x = 4$ 14. 1.30 m
15. \$200/kg   16. 15 km/h

Exercise 2.1

1. (a) $x = 1$ or $x = 3$ (b) $x = -2$ or $x = 4$
   (c) $x = \dfrac{1}{2}$ or $x = 1$ (d) $x = -\dfrac{1}{3}$ or $x = -\dfrac{1}{5}$
   (e) $x = -2$ or $x = \dfrac{3}{2}$ (f) $x = -1$ or $x = \dfrac{5}{3}$
   (g) $x = -\dfrac{3}{4}$ or $x = -\dfrac{1}{2}$ (h) $x = -\dfrac{3}{7}$ or $x = \dfrac{5}{2}$
2. (a) $x = 3$ or $x = 4$ (b) $x = -10$ or $x = 1$
   (c) $x = -\dfrac{5}{2}$ or $x = \dfrac{4}{3}$ (d) $x = -\dfrac{6}{5}$ or $x = \dfrac{6}{5}$
   (e) $x = 0$ or $x = \dfrac{11}{7}$ (f) $x = -1$ or $x = 8$
   (g) $x = 0$ or $x = 3$ (h) $x = -\dfrac{5}{6}$ or $x = -1$
3. 10 cm
4. $x = 6$

Exercise 2.2

1. (c) $x = -1.7$ or $x = 1.7$
2. (c) $x = 2$
3. (c) No real roots
4. (b) $x = -1$ or $x = 3$
5. (b) $x = -2.7$ or $x = 0.2$
6. (b) No real roots
7. (b) 0.2 s and 4.8 s

Exercise 2.3

1. (a) 1   (b) 4   (c) 16   (d) $\dfrac{49}{4}$
   (e) $\dfrac{1}{4}$ (f) $\dfrac{121}{4}$
2. (a) $x = -4$ or $x = 6$ (b) $x = -10$ or $x = 4$
   (c) $x = -\dfrac{3}{2}$ or $x = \dfrac{1}{2}$ (d) $x = 1$ or $x = 4$
   (e) $x = -6.65$ or $x = -1.35$
   (f) $x = -0.162$ or $x = 6.16$
3. (a) $x = -3$ or $x = -1$ (b) $x = 2$ or $x = 6$
   (c) $x = 0.382$ or $x = 2.62$
   (d) $x = -5.37$ or $x = 0.372$
4. (a) $x = 6$ (b) $x = -3$ or $x = 7$
   (c) $x = -7.65$ or $x = 0.65$ (d) $x = -0.62$ or $x = 1.62$
5. (a) $x = -18.7$ or $x = 0.695$ (b) $x = -0.557$ or $x = 12.6$
   (c) $x = -13.7$ or $x = 0.659$ (d) $x = 1$ or $x = 16$
6. 15.4 cm

Exercise 2.4

1. (a) $x = 6$ (b) $x = -2.823$ or $x = -0.177$
   (c) $x = -1$ or $x = 1.667$ (d) No real roots
   (e) $x = -0.611$ or $x = 0.468$ (f) No real roots
2. (a) $x = -0.5$ or $x = 3$ (b) $x = -1.5$ or $x = 1.5$
   (c) No real roots   (d) $x = -1.89$ or $x = 2.39$
3. (a) $x = -2.70$ or $x = 3.70$
   (b) $x = -0.475$ or $x = 2.81$
   (c) $x = 2$ (d) No real roots
4. (a) 50 m   (b) 2 s
   (c) 4.32 s   (d) 3.24 s

Exercise 2.5

1. (a) $x = 1$ (b) $x = -1$ or $x = 3$
   (c) $x = 2$ or $x = 16$ (d) $x = -8$ or $x = 6$
   (e) $x = 2$ or $x = \dfrac{13}{2}$ (f) $x = -\dfrac{9}{5}$ or $x = 5$
   (g) $x = \dfrac{1}{2}$ or $x = 7$ (h) $x = \dfrac{5}{2}$
2. (a) $x = -\dfrac{2}{3}$ or $x = 3$ (b) $x = 0$
   (c) $x = 6$ (d) $x = 2.17$ or $x = -2.77$
   (e) $x = -\dfrac{1}{3}$ or $x = \dfrac{1}{2}$ (f) $x = \dfrac{9}{2}$
3. $\dfrac{3}{4}$ or $\dfrac{4}{3}$
4. $x = 12$

Exercise 2.6

1. 35 and 36
2. 17 and 19
3. 15 cm
4. (a) $(34 - x)$ cm   (b) 23 cm by 11 cm
5. (a) $(x + 5)$ cm   (b) $(x + 5)^2$ cm^2
   (c) $x = 12$
6. (a) (i) $(24 - x)$ cm   (ii) $(17 + x)$ cm
   (iii) $(24 - x)(17 + x)$ cm^2
   (b) $x = 3$ or $x = 4$
7. 2 years
8. 24 cm
9. 26
10. 2.6 cm
11. 2.12 p.m.
12. (a) 60 cm   (b) 35 cm
13. $20
14. 52.3 km/h
15. 5.15 s
16. 30.3 cm
17. 25 people
18. $\dfrac{7}{9}$

Revision Exercise 2

1. (a) $x = -3$ or $x = \dfrac{5}{2}$ (b) $x = -\dfrac{1}{3}$ or $x = 7$
   (c) $x = -\dfrac{5}{3}$ or $x = \dfrac{5}{3}$ (d) $x = \dfrac{3}{4}$ or $x = 2$
2. (a) $x = 0.764$ or $x = 5.24$ (b) $x = -4.65$ or $x = 0.646$
   (c) No real roots   (d) $x = -0.275$ or $x = 7.27$

3. (b) $x = -4.4$ or $x = 1.4$
4. (a) $x = -11$ or $x = 8$ (b) $x = -\dfrac{1}{6}$
   (c) No real roots
   (d) $x = -0.220$ or $x = 1.82$
5. (a) $x = -5$ or $x = 3$ (b) $x = \dfrac{12}{5}$ or $x = \dfrac{9}{2}$
   (c) $x = -1.62$ or $x = 0.618$ (d) $x = -\dfrac{2}{3}$ or $x = \dfrac{5}{7}$
6. (a) $x = -2.18$ or $x = -0.153$ (b) $x = 0$ or $x = 2$
   (c) $x = -3.27$ or $x = 8.27$ (d) $x = -\dfrac{1}{9}$ or $x = \dfrac{1}{6}$
7. 1.86 m
8. 80 km/h
9. (a) $R = r + \dfrac{6}{\pi}$ (b) $r = 3.21$
10. (a) $\dfrac{100}{v}$ h
    (b) (i) $(v + 6)$ km/h   (ii) $\dfrac{100}{v + 6}$ h
    (d) $v \approx -45.5$ or 39.5
    (e) 4 h 44 min
11. (a) $\dfrac{800}{x(x + 4)}$ (b) (i) $\dfrac{200}{x}$ l
    (c) $x \approx 10.81$ or -14.81 (d) 11.8 l
12. (a) (i) $\dfrac{800}{x}$ (ii) $\dfrac{800}{x - 5}$ (iii) $\dfrac{900}{x + 5}$
    (b) $\dfrac{800}{x - 5} - \dfrac{900}{x + 5} = 20$
    (c) 18.9 or -23.9
    (d) 42.4 days

Chapter 3 Linear Inequalities

Try It!

1. $p < 2$
2. (a) $p - 1 < q - 1$ (b) $-4p > -4q$
   (c) $\dfrac{1}{5}p < \dfrac{1}{5}q$
3. $x < 6$
4. $x \geqslant -6$
5. $x \leqslant -11$
6. $x < 2$
7. $-4 < x \leqslant 1$
8. No solution
9. 11 months
10. $54 < x \leqslant 99$

Exercise 3.1

1. (a) True   (b) False   (c) True   (d) False
2. (a) False   (b) True   (c) True   (d) False
3. (a) $<$ (b) $>$ (c) $\leqslant$ (d) $\leqslant$
4. (a) (i) $<$ (ii) $<$
   (b) (i) $\leqslant$ (ii) $\leqslant$

5. (a) $2p - 7 \leqslant 2q - 7$ (b) $-4 - \dfrac{1}{5}p \geqslant -4 - \dfrac{1}{5}q$

6. (a) (i) $a + c < b + c$ (ii) $b + c < b + d$
    (iii) $a + c < b + d$
  (b) Total $> \$7500$

Exercise 3.2

1. (a) $x < 9$ (b) $x \geqslant 1$ (c) $x \leqslant 10$
  (d) $x > 3$ (e) $x \geqslant -1$ (f) $x < 2$
  (g) $x < 2$ (h) $x \leqslant 6$

2. (a) $x > -6$ (b) $x \leqslant \dfrac{29}{6}$ (c) $x > -\dfrac{1}{2}$

  (d) $x > -2$ (e) $x \geqslant 2$ (f) $x \geqslant -\dfrac{31}{33}$

  (g) $x > \dfrac{73}{52}$ (h) $x < -\dfrac{53}{3}$ (i) $x \geqslant \dfrac{31}{4}$

  (j) $x < \dfrac{142}{89}$

3. 1, 2, 3 or 4 hairdryers

Exercise 3.3

1. (a) $x > 5$ (b) $x \leqslant -3$

  (c) No solution   (d) $-\dfrac{4}{3} \leqslant x < 1$

  (e) $x \geqslant 3$ (f) No solution
  (g) $x > 8$ (h) $x \leqslant -7$

2. (a) $x < \dfrac{8}{7}$ (b) No solution

  (c) $-3 < x \leqslant 5$ (d) No solution

  (e) $-\dfrac{11}{2} < x < -\dfrac{1}{3}$ (f) $x \geqslant 6$

3. $-2, -1, 0, 1, 2, 3, 4, 5$
4. -1
5. (a) (i) $19.5 \leqslant x < 20.5$
    (ii) $12.5 \leqslant y < 13.5$
  (b) (i) $64\text{ m} \leqslant \text{perimeter} < 68\text{ m}$
    (ii) $243.75\text{ m}^2 \leqslant \text{area} < 276.75\text{ m}^2$

Exercise 3.4

1. 1, 2, 3, 4, 5 or 6
2. $63 \leqslant$ Ali's score $\leqslant 100$
3. 1, 2, 3, 4, 5 or 6
4. After 5 hours
5. 6 months
6. $4\text{ min} < \text{time} < 7\text{ min}$
7. $6 \leqslant x \leqslant 13$
8. $x > 23$
9. 11 days
10. $\$25$

Revision Exercise 3

1. (a) False   (b) False   (c) True   (d) True
  (e) False
2. (a) True   (b) False   (c) True   (d) False
3. (a) $x < -5$ (b) $x \leqslant -4$

  (c) $x > \dfrac{41}{9}$ (d) $x \leqslant 6$

4. (a) $x > \dfrac{10}{9}$ (b) $x \geqslant -78$

  (c) $x \leqslant -\dfrac{19}{3}$ (d) $x > -4$

5. (a) $x = -\dfrac{5}{3}$ or $x = \dfrac{3}{2}$ (b) $x < -1$

  (c) $-\dfrac{5}{3}$

6. (a) $x < \dfrac{15}{16}$ (b) $-2 \leqslant x < 7$

  (c) No solution
7. (a) $a = 3$ (b) $2 < t < 13$
8. 37 days later
9. 11
10. (a) $(3c - 1)(d - 2e)$ (b) $x = 4.5$

  (c) $x = \dfrac{1}{3}$, $y = -2$

11. (a) $-4 < x < -1$ (b) -2
12. (a) f (b) $a < 4.4$
  (c) $x = 3$; $y = -4$

13. (a) $-5\dfrac{1}{2} < x < 4$ (b) greatest $= 3$, least $= -5$

14. (a) $11\,°C$ (b) $-4, -3$

Chapter 4   Conditions of Congruence and Similarity

Try It!

1. (a) $\triangle ABM \equiv \triangle ACM$ (SSS)   (b) $60°$
2. (a) $\triangle ABC \equiv \triangle DEC$ (SAS)   (b) 8 cm
3. (a) $\angle MLN = 45°$, $\angle UTV = 45°$
  (b) $\triangle LMN \equiv \triangle TUV$ (ASA)
4. (a) $\triangle ABD \equiv \triangle CDB$ (RHS)   (b) $25°$
5. (a) (i) $\angle APQ$ (ii) $\angle AQP$
  (b) $\triangle APQ$ is similar to $\triangle ABC$.
      (Angle-Angle-Angle similarity)
  (c) $x = 3$
6. (a) Side-Side-Side similarity
  (b) $104°$
7. (a) Side-Angle-Side similarity
  (b) $y = 13.5$
8. $x = 6\dfrac{2}{3}$, $y = 20$

9. (a) $2 : 5$ (b) $4 : 25$
  (c) 6 cm^2 (d) 31.5 cm^2
10. $5 : 8$
11. (a) $5 : 7$ (b) $125 : 343$
  (c) 250 g
12. (a) 4 cm   (b) $12\pi\text{ cm}^3$
  (c) $84\pi\text{ cm}^3$

Exercise 4.1

1. (a) $\triangle ABC \equiv \triangle YZX$ (SSS)   (b) $\triangle DEF \equiv \triangle GHK$ (SAS)
  (c) $\triangle LMN \equiv \triangle QPR$ (ASA)   (d) $\triangle STU \equiv \triangle WXY$ (RHS)
2. (a) $\triangle ABC \equiv \triangle FED$ (ASA)   (b) $\triangle GHK \equiv \triangle LMN$ (SAS)
  (c) $\triangle PQR \equiv \triangle SUT$ (SSS)   (d) $\triangle VWX \equiv \triangle AZY$ (RHS)
3. (a) not congruent   (b) $\triangle GHK \equiv \triangle LNM$ (SSS)
  (c) not congruent   (d) $\triangle VWX \equiv \triangle AYZ$ (ASA)
4. (a) (i) $\triangle ABC \equiv \triangle CDA$ (ii) SSS   (iii) $118°$
  (b) (i) $\triangle EFH \equiv \triangle GFH$ (ii) SAS   (iii) 4

(c) (i) $\triangle KLM \equiv \triangle NPM$ (ii) RHS (iii) 54°
(d) (i) $\triangle RST \equiv \triangle SRV$ (ii) ASA (iii) 9
5. (a) $\triangle ABM \equiv \triangle DCM$ (SAS) (b) 64 m
6. (a) $\triangle ABC \equiv \triangle EDC$ (ASA) (b) 40 m

Exercise 4.2

1. (a) $\triangle ABC$ is similar to $\triangle DEF$. (Angle-Angle-Angle similarity)
   (b) $\triangle GHK$ is similar to $\triangle NLM$. (Angle-Angle-Angle similarity)
   (c) $\triangle PQR$ is similar to $\triangle STU$. (Side-Side-Side similarity)
   (d) $\triangle VWX$ is similar to $\triangle YZA$. (Side-Angle-Side similarity)
2. (a) $\triangle ABC$ is similar to $\triangle DFE$. (Angle-Angle-Angle similarity)
   (b) not similar
   (c) insufficient information
   (d) $\triangle VWX$ is similar to $\triangle ZYA$. (Side-Angle-Side similarity)
3. (a) (i) $\triangle ABE$ is similar to $\triangle CBD$.
                (Angle-Angle-Angle similarity)
      (ii) 18
   (b) (i) $\triangle ABC$ is similar to $\triangle AMN$.
                (Side-Angle-Side similarity)
      (ii) 4
   (c) (i) $\triangle ABC$ is similar to $\triangle DEC$.
                (Angle-Angle-Angle similarity)
      (ii) $3\frac{1}{3}$
   (d) (i) $\triangle ABC$ is similar to $\triangle AQP$.
                (Angle-Angle-Angle similarity)
      (ii) 11.6
4. (a) Angle-Angle-Angle similarity
   (b) 3 (c) $4\frac{2}{3}$
5. (a) $\triangle BCE$ is similar to $\triangle ACF$. (Angle-Angle-Angle similarity)
   (b) 15
   (c) 37.5
6. (a) $\triangle AEF$ is similar to $\triangle ABC$; $\triangle ACD$ is similar to $\triangle FCG$.
   (b) 2 : 1
   (c) 4
7. 2.25 m
8. (a) $\triangle ABM$ is similar to $\triangle CDM$.
                (Angle-Angle-Angle similarity)
   (b) 3 m
9. (a) $\triangle PQR$ is similar to $\triangle TSR$.
                (Angle-Angle-Angle similarity)
   (b) 18 m

Exercise 4.3

1. (a) $A_1 = 3.375$ cm^2 (b) $A_2 = 400$ cm^2
   (c) $A_2 = 125.44$ cm^2 (d) $A_1 = 81$ cm^2
   (e) $A_2 = 112.5$ cm^2 (f) $A_1 = 201.6$ cm^2
2. (a) 3 (b) 12 (c) 10 (d) 24
3. (a) 1 : 2 (b) 1 : 4
4. (a) 2 : 3 (b) 4 : 9
5. 22.5 cm^2
6. (a) $\triangle ABE$ is similar to $\triangle CBD$. (Side-Angle-Side similarity)
   (b) 117 cm^2
7. (a) Angle-Angle-Angle similarity
   (b) 112 cm^2 (c) 49 cm^2
8. (a) 2 : 5 (b) 21 cm
9. (b) (i) 2 : 3 (ii) 4 : 9
   (c) 45 min

10. 112 cm^2
11. (a) 90° (b) 4 m (c) 12 m^2 (d) 6.75 m^2

Exercise 4.4

1. (a) $V_1 = 53\frac{1}{3}$ cm^3 (b) $V_2 = 1800$ cm^3
   (c) $V_1 = 1130\frac{5}{8}$ cm^3 (d) $V_2 = 1555.2$ cm^3
2. (a) 1 : 2   1 : 4   1 : 8
   (b) 2 : 3   4 : 9   8 : 27
   (c) 5 : 6   25 : 36   125 : 216
3. (a) 7 : 6 (b) 343 : 216 (c) 1029 cm^3
4. (a) 4 : 9 (b) 8 : 27 (c) 240 cm^2
5. (a) 4250 cm^3
   (b) (i) 244.8 cm^2 (ii) 7344 cm^3
6. (a) 75 cm^2 (b) 5 : 7 (c) 22.638 kg
7. 960 g
8. (a) 327 (b) 54 cm^2
9. (a) 9 : 16 : 25 (b) 27 : 64 : 125 (c) 12 cm
10. (a) 1 : 7 : 19 (b) 1 : 3 : 5 (c) 140 cm^3

Revision Exercise 4

1. (a) $\triangle ABC \equiv \triangle YXZ$ (SAS) (b) $\triangle PQR \equiv \triangle YZX$ (ASA)
   (c) $\triangle PQR \equiv \triangle YZX$ (SAS)
2. (a) $\triangle ABC \equiv \triangle ADC$ (SAS) (b) $\triangle ABC \equiv \triangle ADC$ (ASA)
   (c) $\triangle ABC \equiv \triangle DEC$ (SAS) (d) $\triangle ABD \equiv \triangle CDB$ (SSS)
3. (a) $\triangle ADM \equiv \triangle CBM$ (SSS) (b) $\triangle AEM \equiv \triangle CFM$ (ASA)
   (c) $\triangle BEM \equiv \triangle DFM$ (ASA) or $\triangle ABM \equiv \triangle CDM$ (SSS)
4. (a) $\triangle ABC \equiv \triangle ADC$ (SAS) (b) 27 m
5. (a) $\triangle ABC$ is similar to $\triangle RPQ$.
   (b) $\triangle ABC$ is similar to $\triangle ZYX$.
   (c) $\triangle PQR$ is similar to $\triangle YZX$.
6. (a) $\triangle ABC$ is similar to $\triangle CBD$, $x = 2\frac{1}{4}$
   (b) $\triangle ABC$ is similar to $\triangle EDC$, $x = 10$
   (c) $\triangle ABE$ is similar to $\triangle ACD$, $x = 9$
   (d) $\triangle ABC$ is similar to $\triangle ACD$, $x = 9$
7. (a) $\triangle ABE$ is similar to $\triangle CBD$ (Angle-Angle-Angle similarity)
   (b) (i) 15 cm (ii) 7.5 cm (iii) 25.5 cm
8. (a) $\triangle ABD$ is similar to $\triangle CAD$.
                (Angle-Angle-Angle similarity)
   (b) 6 cm (c) $\sqrt{117}$ cm (d) 12 cm^2
9. (a) $\triangle ABC$ is similar to $\triangle APQ$.
                (Angle-Angle-Angle similarity)
   (b) 17.5 cm (c) 110.25 cm^2 (d) 7.5 cm
   (e) (i) 20.25 cm^2 (ii) 54 cm^2
10. (a) 7 : 9 (b) 49 : 81
11. (a) 4 : 5 (b) 204.8 g
12. (a) 392π cm^3 (b) 49π cm^3
    (c) 116.375π cm^3
13. (a) 15 cm (b) 1 : 1
14. (a) 1080 cm^2 (b) 2 : 3 (c) $10\frac{2}{3}$ kg
16. (b) (i) $8\frac{2}{3}$ cm (ii) $\frac{9}{49}$
17. (b) (i) 9.16 (ii) 3.14

Chapter 5 Functions and Graphs

Try It!

4. (b) 30 vases; $900
5. (b) The graph of $y = -x^3$ is the reflection of the graph of $y = x^3$ about the x-axis.
8. (b) $x = 2.8$
9. (b) $(1.3, 1.89)$
11. (a) (i) 60 cells   (ii) 240 cells
    (c) 2.7 hours
12. (b) (i) -2 (ii) 0   (iii) 4
13. (a) (i) $h = \dfrac{100}{x^2}$

     (c) (i) $x = 3.8$ and 8.5 (ii) -17
         (iii) $5.8 \text{ cm} \times 5.8 \text{ cm} \times 2.97 \text{ cm}$

Exercise 5.1

1. (a) $(0, 2)$ (b) $(-1, 0)$
    (c) $(3, 4)$ (d) $(-2, -5)$
2. (a) $x = 0$ (b) $x = 4$
    (c) $x = -1$ (d) $x = 2$
3. (a) x-intercepts: 1, 4   (b) x-intercepts: -3, 1
         y-intercept: 4 y-intercept: -3
    (c) x-intercepts: -2, -3 (d) x-intercepts: 0, -5
         y-intercept: -6 y-intercept: 0
4. (a) (i) $y = (x + 1)^2 + 2$ (ii) Minimum point $(-1, 2)$
    (b) (i) $y = -(x - 4)^2 + 11$ (ii) Maximum point $(4, 11)$

     (c) (i) $y = -\left(x - \dfrac{5}{2}\right)^2 + \dfrac{25}{4}$

         (ii) Maximum point $\left(\dfrac{5}{2}, \dfrac{25}{4}\right)$

     (d) (i) $y = \left(x - \dfrac{7}{2}\right)^2 - 6.25$

         (ii) Minimum point $(3.5, -6.25)$
5. (a) (i) $y = (x + 4)(x - 1)$
         (ii) Minimum point $(-1.5, -6.25)$
    (b) (i) $y = -(x - 1)(x - 2)$
         (ii) Maximum point $(1.5, 0.25)$
    (c) (i) $y = -(x + 1)^2$ (ii) Maximum point $(-1, 0)$
    (d) (i) $y = (x + 2)(x - 2)$ (ii) Minimum point $(0, -4)$
6. (a) $x + 7$ (b) $y = x(x + 7)$
    (d) -12.25; -3.5 and 3.5
7. (b) 20 items; $400

Exercise 5.2

3. (a) $\dfrac{2}{3}$ (c) $\dfrac{2}{3}$
5. (a) -2
6. (b) $(1, 1)$ and $(-1, -1)$

     (c) The graph of $y = \dfrac{1}{x}$ is symmetrical about the line $y = x$.

7. (a) $y = \dfrac{4}{x}$

8. (b) 75% decrease   (c) F increases to infinity.

Exercise 5.3

3. (b) $x = 1$
4. (b) Maximum point $(1, 4)$; Minimum point $(-1, 0)$

5. (b) $x = -0.4$, $x = -1$ or $x = -2.6$
6. (b) $(-1, 0)$ (c) $x = -1.5$, -0.8 or 1.8
7. (b) $x = -1.6$ or 0.6
8. (b) (i) 9.6 units, 2.9 hours
         (ii) 1.3 hours and 4.2 hours

Exercise 5.4

3. (b) $x = 1.4$
4. (b) $x = 1.8$
5. (b) $x = 0.9$
6. (a) (i) $50 000   (ii) $1 350 000
    (c) 2.7 years

Exercise 5.5

1. (a) 1.4   (b) -2 (c) 0   (d) -2
2. (b) (i) 0   (ii) 8
3. (a) (i) 0   (ii) 3
4. (b) $-\dfrac{1}{2}$
5. (b) $(-0.5, -0.25)$ (c) 0
6. (b) (i) 0   (ii) -3
    (c) $(2, -7)$
7. (b) $(1, 2)$ (c) (i) 0   (ii) 3.5
    (d) $x = 0.7$ and 1.6
8. (b) Maximum point $(1.7, 10.4)$; Minimum point $(-1.7, -10.4)$
    (c) -10 (d) $-1.7 < x < 1.7$
    (e) (ii) $x = -2.5$, 0 and 2.5
9. (a) $\dfrac{1}{2}$ (c) 20
    (d) (i) 50 printers   (ii) $16
    (e) (ii) 15 or 61 printers
10. (a) (i) $\dfrac{50}{x}$ cm   (ii) $(x - 3)$ cm

        (iii) $\left(\dfrac{50}{x} - 2\right)$ cm

     (c) (i) 19.5
     (d) (i) 6.6   (ii) 7.5
        (iii) 8.7   (iv) 21.3 cm^2

Revision Exercise 5

1. (a) $A(-4, 0)$ (b) $x = -2$
    (c) $(-2, -4)$ (d) $x > -2$
2. (a) $x = 1$ or $x = 3$ (b) $-(x - 2)^2 + 1$
    (d) $(2, 1)$ (e) 0
3. (a) -6.875
    (c) (i) Minimum point $(1.8, -8.2)$;
             Maximum point $(-1.1, 4.1)$
         (ii) 15
    (d) (ii) $x = -2$, -0.2 and 3.6
4. (c) -18
    (d) (i) $x = 0.7$ and 5.1 (ii) No solution
    (e) 13.9

     (f) (ii) $x^2 + \dfrac{20}{x} = -8x + 40$

5. (a) $h = 18 - 2x$ (d) -45
    (e) (i) $x = 3.8$ and 7.7 (ii) $x = 6$
6. (c) -1.5
7. (a) (i) $p = 12$; $q = 0$ (iii) $x = 0.55$ or 3.85
    (b) 5.04   (d) $x^3 - 3x^2 - 5x + 10 = 0$

8. (a) $n = -1$
10. (a) $p = -44.4$
    (d) (i) 25 m   (ii) 1.95 s
    (e) (i) −17.5
    (f) 24 m
11. (b) (i) $p = 105\frac{1}{3}$
    (c) $r = 2.25$ or 5.7
    (d) Gradient ≈ -42.3
    (e) (i) $r = 3.7$ (ii) 81.5 cm^2

Chapter 6   Properties of Circles
Try It!

1. 17 cm
2. (a) 13 cm   (b) 5.25 cm
3. 7 cm
4. 55°
5. 100°
6. 34°
7. 66°
8. $\angle ADB = 54°$, $\angle DAB = 73°$
9. $\angle x = 53°$, $\angle y = 37°$
10. 103°
11. 30°
12. 110°
13. (a) 80°   (b) 40°
14. 2.5 cm
15. $AQ = 5$ cm, $BP = 10$ cm
16. (a) 50°   (b) 65°

Exercise 6.1

1. (a) 12 cm   (b) 27.5 cm
2. (a) 13 cm   (b) 7.62 cm
3. (a) 8 cm   (b) 10.2 cm
4. (a) 9 cm   (b) 41 cm
5. 3.89 cm
6. (a) Yes
    (b) (i) 20 cm (ii) 42 cm   (iii) 6 cm
7. (a) 37 cm   (b) 420 cm^2
8. (c) 8 cm
9. 5 m
10. 13.8 cm

Exercise 6.2

1. (a) 100°   (b) 40°   (c) 115°   (d) 132°
2. (a) 60°   (b) 133°   (c) 45°   (d) 31°
3. (a) 99°   (b) 51°   (c) 27°   (d) 53°
4. (a) $\angle x = 38°$, $\angle y = 71°$ (b) $\angle x = 27°$, $\angle y = 63°$
    (c) $\angle x = 40°$, $\angle y = 110°$ (d) $\angle x = 60°$, $\angle y = 90°$
5. 34°
6. 29°
7. (a) 30 m   (b) 240 m^2 (c) $14\frac{2}{17}$ m
    (d) 15 m
8. (a) ASA   (b) Yes   (c) 55°

9. (a) $\triangle ADE$ is similar to $\triangle BCE$. (Angle-Angle-Angle similarity)
    (b) $16\frac{2}{3}$

Exercise 6.3

1. (a) $\angle x = 64°$, $\angle y = 116°$ (b) $\angle x = 73°$, $\angle y = 107°$
    (c) $\angle x = 108°$, $\angle y = 37°$ (d) $\angle x = 68°$, $\angle y = 112°$
    (e) $\angle x = 35°$ (f) $\angle x = 105°$
    (g) $\angle x = 127°$ (h) $\angle x = 109°$
2. (a) 108°   (b) 62°
3. (a) 118°   (b) 31°
4. 32°
5. (a) 105°   (b) 103°
6. 58°
7. (a) $\triangle ABC \equiv \triangle ABD$ (RHS)   (b) 130°
8. (b) Yes   (c) 12 cm   (d) 156 cm^2
9. (b) $\triangle ACE$ is similar to $\triangle DCB$. (Angle-Angle-Angle similarity)
    (c) 12 cm

Exercise 6.4

1. (a) 58°   (b) 35°   (c) 37°   (d) 40°
2. 10 cm
3. $2\frac{2}{3}$ cm
4. (a) $\angle x = 65°$, $\angle y = 25°$ (b) $\angle x = 27°$, $\angle y = 126°$
    (c) $\angle x = 52°$ (d) $\angle x = 63°$, $\angle y = 126°$
5. (a) 29 cm   (b) 23°
6. 7.75 cm
7. $AR = 5$ cm, $CQ = 7$ cm
8. $AP = 30$ cm, $CQ = 10$ cm
9. $\angle x = 67°$, $\angle y = 59°$, $\angle z = 54°$
10. 29.2 cm
12. (a) ASA   (b) 52.0 cm

Revision Exercise 6

1. (a) 3 cm   (b) 4 cm   (c) 5 cm
2. (a) 5 cm   (b) 12 cm   (c) 13 cm
3. (a) 55°   (b) 125°   (c) 27.5°
4. (a) 26°   (b) 93°   (c) 76°
5. (a) 36°   (b) 36°   (c) 144°   (d) 108°
6. (a) 32°   (b) 32°   (c) 79°   (d) 47°
7. (a) 35°   (b) 55°   (c) 23°   (d) 32°
8. (a) 123°   (b) 53°   (c) 73°   (d) 33°
9. (a) (i) $90° - \theta$ (ii) $45° - \dfrac{\theta}{2}$ (iii) $45° + \dfrac{\theta}{2}$
    (b) $4\frac{1}{8}$ cm
10. (a) $\triangle BNT$ (SAS)   (b) 90°
    (c) 61°   (d) 30.5°
11. (a) $OM = (10 - r)$ m   (b) 5.8 m
12. (a) $\angle ABC$ and $\angle OBT$
    (b) (i) 34°   (ii) 124°   (iii) 34°
13. (b) 30°
    (c) (i) 68°   (ii) 96°
14. (a) (i) 5 cm   (ii) 22.6°
    (b) (i) 70°   (ii) 64°
    (iii) 55°